FORESTRY COMMISSION BULLETIN 124

An Ecological Site Classification for Forestry in Great Britain

Graham Pyatt, Duncan Ray and Jane Fletcher

Woodland Ecology Branch, Forest Research,
Northern Research Station, Roslin, Midlothian, EH25 9SY

Edinburgh: Forestry Commission

ISBN 0 85538 418 2

Pyatt, G.; Ray, D.; Fletcher, J. 2001
An Ecological Site Classification for Forestry in Great Britain. Bulletin 124.
Forestry Commission, Edinburgh.

FDC 542:111.82:(410)

KEYWORDS: Climate, Ecology, Forestry, Indicator plants, Soils, Site types

Acknowledgements

The climatic data used in this work were obtained from the UK Meteorological
Office under a licence agreement. We are indebted to Messrs Stewart Wass and
George Anderson for their help in this matter. We are grateful to the Climatic
Research Unit of the University of East Anglia (David Viner and Elaine Barrow) for
making available the 10 x 10 gridded datasets under the Climate Impacts Link
Project of the UK Department of the Environment, Transport and the Regions.

Gary White and Tom Connolly respectively assisted with the GIS and statistical
work involved in the preparation of the climatic datasets and Karen Purdy helped in
the preparation of the map of windiness. We thank the various colleagues in Forest
Research who helped with the preparation of the Figures.

The species suitability criteria have been subjected to the scrutiny and approval of
a panel of 'three wise men', Bill Mason, Head of Silviculture (North) Branch, Alan
Fletcher, former Head of Tree Improvement Branch and Derek Redfern, former
Head of Pathology (North) Section.

Gary Kerr of Silviculture and Seed Research Branch and Christopher Quine, Head
of Woodland Ecology Branch, read the draft and suggested many improvements. As
former Head of Woodland Ecology Branch, Simon Hodge guided the progress of
ESC for several years.

Contents

List of Figures

List of Tables *Page*

An Ecological Site Classification for Forestry in Great Britain

Summary

Ecological Site Classification (ESC) will help forest managers to select tree species, and to make related decisions based on an appreciation of the ecological potential of sites. The classification focuses on the key factors of site that influence tree growth, and that are important to the rest of the ecosystem. This site-orientated approach to tree species selection will assist users to practise sustainable forestry. For example, by selecting species suitable to a site it will discourage the approach of selecting a species and then altering site conditions by excessive ground preparation and fertilizer applications.

The multi-dimensional approach to site classification, assessing four climate and two soil factors, is similar to that adopted in the Biogeoclimatic Ecosystem Classification (BEC) of British Columbia. However, unlike BEC, it is applicable to all kinds of woodlands, from plantations of a single species through to semi-natural woodlands, as well as to many kinds of non-wooded land. The close link between ESC and the National Vegetation Classification (NVC) provides clear evidence of the ecological requirements of different vegetation communities on a given site.

This Bulletin contains a full description of the methodology behind ESC, and provides an explanatory foundation for users of the software ESC-DSS. It is recommended reading for forest managers, woodland owners, academics, students and others concerned with the ecological potential of site types in Britain.

Une Classification Écologique des Stations pour la Foresterie de Grande-Bretagne

Résumé

La Classification Ecologique des Stations (ESC) aidera les gestionnaires des forêts à sélectionner les essences et à prendre des décisions s'y rattachant en se basant sur une évaluation du potentiel écologique des stations. Cette classification est centrée sur les facteurs-clés présentés par une station, des facteurs qui influencent la croissance des arbres et sont importants pour le reste de l'écosystème. Cette approche de la sélection des essences, axée sur la station, aidera ses utilisateurs à pratiquer une foresterie durable. Par exemple, en permettant de sélectionner des essences convenant à la station, cette approche découragera l'approche consistant à choisir une essence, et à transformer ensuite les conditions de la station par une préparation du sol et des applications d'engrais excessives.

Cette approche multidimensionnelle de la classification de la station, qui évalue quatre facteurs climatiques et deux facteurs liés au sol ressemble à l'approche adoptée par la Classification des Ecosystèmes Biogéoclimatiques (BEC) utilisée en Colombie britannique. Néanmoins, à la différence de l'approche BEC, elle s'applique à toutes sortes de bois -- des plantations ne comprenant qu'une seule essence aux bois semi-naturels --, ainsi qu'à de nombreux types de terres non-boisées. Le lien étroit existant entre ESC et la Classification de la Végétation Nationale (NVC) montre clairement les critèria écologiques des différentes associations végétales sur une station donnée.

Ce Bulletin contient la description complète de la méthodologie ayant amené à ESC et fournit une introduction explicative s'adressant aux utilisateurs du logiciel ESC-DSS. Sa lecture est recommandée aux gestionnaires de forêts, propriétaires de bois, universitaires, étudiants et à toute personne concernée par le potentiel écologique des types de stations existant en Grande-Bretagne.

Ökologische Standortklassifizierung für die Forstwirtschaft in Großbritannien

Zusammenfassung

Ökologische Standortklassifizierung (ESC) hilft Forstmanagern, Baumarten auszuwählen und damit verbundene Entscheidungen zu treffen, indem sie sich auf eine Bewertung des ökologischen Potentials eines Standortes basiert. Die Klassifizierung konzentriert sich auf einige Schlüsselfaktoren des Standortes, die den Baumwuchs beeinflussen und für das restliche Ökosystem wichtig sind. Diese standort-bezogene Methode zur Baumartenwahl wird es dem Benutzer erleichtern, nachhaltige Forstwirtschaft zu betreiben. Durch die Auswahl von Arten die dem Standort angebracht sind, wird es zum Beispiel verhindert eine Art auszuwählen und dann die Standortbedingungen durch übermäßige Bodenbearbeitung und Düngeanwendung zu verändern.

Die multidimensionale Methode der Standortklassifizierung bewertet vier klimatische und zwei Bodenfaktoren und ähnelt damit der Biogeoklimatischen Ökosystem Klassifizierung (BEC) von Britisch Kolumbien. Sie ist jedoch, im Gegensatz zu BEC, für alle Waldarten, von Plantagen einer einzigen Art bis zu naturnahen Wäldern, aber auch für viele Arten von unbewaldetem Land anwendbar. Die enge Verbindung zwischen ESC und der Nationalen Vegetationsklassifizierung (NVC) liefert klare Beweise der ökologischen Bedürfnisse verschiedener Vegetationsgemeinschaften an einem bestimmten Standort.

Dieses Bulletin enthält eine volle Beschreibung der Methologie hinter ESC, und liefert eine Erklärungsgrundlage für Benutzer des Computerprogrammes ESC-DSS. Es ist empfohlener Lesestoff für Forstmanager, Waldbesitzer, Akademiker, Studenten und andere, die sich mit dem ökologischem Potential der Standortarten in Britannien befassen.

Dosbarthiad Safleoedd Ecolegol ar gyfer Coedwigaeth ym Mhrydain Fawr

Crynodeb

Bydd Dosbarthiad Safleoedd Ecolegol (ESC) o gymorth i reolwyr coedwig er mwyn dewis rhywogaethau coed ac i wneud penderfyniadau sy'n gysylltiedig â hynny, penderfyniadau fyddai'n seiliedig ar werthfawrogiad o bosibiliadau ecolegol y safleoedd. Mae'r dosbarthu yn canolbwyntio ar ffactorau allweddol safleoedd sy'n dylanwadu ar dwf coed ac sy'n bwysig i weddill yr ecosystem. Bydd y dull hwn o gyfeirio at safleoedd wrth ddewis rhywogaethau coed yn cynorthwyo defnyddwyr i arfer coedwigaeth gynaliadwy. Er enghraifft, drwy ddewis rhywogaeth sy'n addas ar gyfer y safle, ni anogir y dull o ddethol rhywogaeth ac wedyn newid cyflwr y safle ar gyfer y rhywogaeth honno drwy orbaratoi'r ddaear a defnyddio gwrtaith yn ormodol.

Mae'r dull amlochrog tuag at ddosbarthu safleoedd, gan asesu pedwar ffactor hinsawdd a dau ffactor pridd, yn debyg i'r un a fabwysiadwyd yn Nosbarthiad Ecosystem Fioddaearhinsoddegol (BEC) Columbia Brydeinig. Fodd bynnag, yn wahanol i BEC, mae'n berthnasol i bob math o goetiroedd, o blanhigfeydd un rhywogaeth ymlaen i goetiroedd lled-naturiol, yn ogystal ag i lawer math o dir di-goed. Mae'r cyswllt agos rhwng ESC a'r Dosbarthiad Planhigion Cenedlaethol (NVC) yn rhoi tystiolaeth glir o anghenion ecolegol gwahanol gymunedau o blanhigion ar safle penodol.

Mae'r Bwletin hwn yn cynnwys disgrifiad llawn o'r fethodoleg y tu ôl i ESC, ac mae'n rhoi sail esboniadol ar gyfer defnyddwyr meddalwedd ESC-DSS. Anogir ei ddarllen gan reolwyr coedwig, perchnogion coetiroedd, academyddion, myfyrwyr ac eraill sy'n ymddiddori yn y posibiliadau ecolegol a geir mewn mathau o safleoedd ym Mhrydain.

Chapter 1

Introduction

This classification will help forest managers make decisions on silviculture and other aspects of land use based on an appreciation of the ecological potential of sites. It is applicable to all kinds of woodland, from plantations of a single species through to semi-natural woodlands, and to many kinds of non-wooded land. Ecological Site Classification (ESC) incorporates the existing classification of forest soil types that has been the basis of silviculture for many years (Pyatt, 1970, 1977). The new classification focuses on the key factors of site that influence tree growth, and are important to the rest of the ecosystem and its sustainable development. The new classification is therefore designed to support current forest policy (Forestry Commission, 1998).

ESC provides a method of assessing site in a practical, cost-effective and, as far as is possible, quantitative way. The classification assumes that three principal factors determine site: climate, soil moisture regime and soil nutrient regime. The three factors can be thought of as forming the axes of a cube (Figure 1). For Britain as a whole the climate axis is divided into seven zones, and there are eight classes of soil moisture regime and six classes of soil nutrient regime. The combination of moisture and nutrient regimes is referred to as soil quality, the grid formed from these axes being the soil quality grid. This three dimensional approach to site classification is similar to that adopted in the Biogeoclimatic Ecosystem Classification of British Columbia (Pojar *et al.*, 1987) and previously encouraged in Britain by Anderson (1950), Anderson and Fairbairn (1955) and Fairbairn (1960). Similar soil quality grids but with less formal climatic classifications are in widespread use in Europe (Ellenberg, 1988; Anon., 1991a and b; Rameau *et al.*, 1989, 1993).

An individual site type, typically a homogeneous stand of ground vegetation or patch of soil with an area of 10 m^2 – 5 ha, will occupy one, or at most two cells of the cube of Figure 1. The site type will have a range of soil quality encompassed by one class (or at most two adjacent classes) of moisture and nutrient regime, within whichever climatic zone it lies. The classification contains a finite number of site types, as represented by each cell within the cube of Figure 1, that is 7 x 8 x 6 = 336. An individual forest will usually lie within one climatic zone and typically cover less than half of the soil quality grid, giving fewer than 24 site types. However, site types within one forest need not occupy contiguous cells, as there may be gaps in the coverage of the grid.

Use of the classification for an individual site involves three stages: the first is to identify the site type, the second is to consider the various silvicultural and ecological options possible for that site type, the third is to decide on the appropriate management of the site in the light of the objectives. ESC provides the means to accomplish the first step of the process and the second step as far as choice of species or native woodland type. In due course further ecological choices and other aspects of site-related forest management will be added to the classification.

This Bulletin provides an explanatory and supporting framework for the Decision Support System (a compact disc with software referred to as the *ESC Decision Support System* or *ESC-DSS*; Forestry Commission, 2001), but does not attempt to duplicate its content. It provides a comprehensive description of ESC but not a manual method for performing site analysis. Potential users of ESC are encouraged to obtain an understanding of the classification from this Bulletin and then explore the ESC-DSS.

Within the Bulletin, Chapters 2, 3 and 4 explain the basis for the classification of the three principal components, climate, soil moisture regime and soil nutrient regime. Chapters 5 and 6 explain how indirect methods are used to evaluate soil quality. The final chapters 7 and 8 show how the site suitability of individual tree species and types of native woodland has been worked out, enabling land managers to make choices based on sound ecological principles.

This Bulletin and the ESC-DSS replace Technical Paper 20 (Pyatt and Suárez, 1997) and incorporate several major improvements to the system. The climate data are now available for the whole of Britain and have been updated to the recording period 1961–90; a map of windiness for the whole of Britain has been prepared. Recent research has established the chemical basis of soil nutrient regime and has provided a method of assessing soil nutrient regime from the ground vegetation (Wilson, 1998).

In spite of all this work ESC is not yet as good as we would like it to be. The prediction of soil nutrient regime is based on too few sample plots to give adequate precision at the Very Poor end of the range, consequently the assessment of such sites draws support from an earlier method (Taylor, 1991). The prediction of the yield class likely to be achieved by tree species in pure stands is based on a method that is not yet validated. Further work is underway to extend the ecological and silvicultural choices provided by ESC site types, to develop a system linked to a Geographical Information System (GIS) and to improve the predictions of soil nutrient regime and yield class. The application of GIS and availability of digital soil maps will be of crucial importance to the effective use of ESC at the forest scale. An example of the benefits of this approach to examine the potential effects of different management strategies has been provided by the New Forest, Hampshire (Pyatt *et al.*, 2001).

Chapter 2
Climate

Importance and choice of factors

Climate is important to foresters because it limits the means by which they can achieve their objectives of management. Aspects of climate constrain the variety of tree species that can be planted, although in much of Britain the choice is wide compared with many temperate areas. The climate, especially the available light and energy (warmth), sets an upper limit to the rate of tree growth and timber yield. Equally, climate controls the other parts of the forest ecosystem, whether they be biological, hydrological or pedological and sets the limits within which sustainable management can be practised.

Bio-climatic maps have previously been published for Scotland (Birse and Dry, 1970; Birse and Robertson, 1970; Birse, 1971) and for England and Wales (Bendelow and Hartnup, 1980). These maps, mostly at the 1:625 000 scale, are familiar to many foresters, but the small scale has limited their practical use to national or regional research studies. The climatic factors chosen for ESC are similar to those incorporated in these maps but are based on a larger set of meteorological stations and modern methods of interpolation.

Four climatic factors are currently used in ESC: 'warmth', 'wetness', 'continentality' and 'windiness'. Warmth and wetness are the most important factors and are combined to define climatic zones of relevance particularly to choice of species. Continentality and windiness may refine species choice and the latter can have a major influence on timber production. All four factors are therefore required to describe the climatic conditions for tree growth at a site. A fifth climatic factor is under development (see the final section of this chapter entitled 'Winter cold, unseasonable frosts and other winter hazards'). Solar radiation in terms of light level and duration

is vital for photosynthesis and therefore growth is dependent on factors such as latitude, aspect, slope and cloud cover. Evidence that solar radiation directly, rather than indirectly through temperature effects, limits tree growth in Britain is, however, lacking at present. The adjustments to accumulated temperature and soil moisture regime suggested in Tables 1 and 7 take account of some of the effects of variation in solar radiation.

Except for windiness, the climatic factors have been calculated from data for the recording period 1961–90 supplied by the Meteorological Office, in most cases via the Climatic Research Unit (CRU) at the University of East Anglia. The CRU dataset consists of a number of basic meteorological variables (monthly mean temperature, monthly rainfall, etc.) for each 10 x 10 km square throughout Britain (Barrow et al., 1993). Values for each climatic factor have been calculated for the 2836 squares, then the values have been interpolated to a finer resolution. The ESC-DSS supplies values for any 100 x 100 m grid reference in Britain. The climate maps included in this publication are mainly for illustration purposes and should not be used to read off a climatic value for a particular site. In order to reduce the map datasets to a manageable size, accuracy has been reduced.

Warmth

It is widely understood that summer or growing season warmth is a major determinant of tree growth rate. For small areas of the country relative warmth is conveniently approximated by elevation but at larger scales latitude and longitude are also necessary to predict warmth. Accumulated day-degrees above a 'growth threshold' temperature provide a convenient measure of summer warmth. ESC follows a number of temperate or boreal countries in using a threshold temperature of $5.0^{\circ}C$, whereas previous British maps used $5.6^{\circ}C$. To interpolate the values of accumulated temperature a formula was obtained relating the value for each 10 km square to its easting, northing, elevation and distance from the sea, based on a Digital Elevation Model obtained from the Ordnance Survey (White *et al.*, 2000). Final processing of the data to compile the map (Figure 2) was done using a raster GIS.

The interpolation formula accounts for trends of accumulated temperature decreasing with elevation, northing and easting but there is no influence of distance from sea. The formula also allows that the *rate* of decrease with elevation (the 'lapse rate') is greatest in the south of the country. The user of the ESC-DSS is able to explore these trends in the data. The range of accumulated temperature above $5.0^{\circ}C$ (AT5) in Britain is from 0 to 2000 day-degrees. This range is divided into nine classes in order to aid the recognition of 'lowland' or warm zones, 'upland' or cool zones, 'sub-alpine' and 'alpine' zones. Most of our commonly used tree species grow well in the warm zones, but are restricted in growth where the climate is cool. Few species can tolerate the sub-alpine climate and their growth is extremely slow. The alpine climate is incapable of sustaining tree growth.

The map and the dataset which it illustrates are strictly applicable only to level sites. Sloping sites, depending on their gradient and aspect (the compass direction they face) receive different amounts of direct radiation from the sun and may be warmer or cooler than level sites under some conditions. Although the amount of radiation received by a slope can be estimated it is not possible to predict the air or soil temperature that will result because of the altitudinal effect and heat transfers by wind and convection. Measurements of temperature on different slopes have been few but permit a very simple model to be developed for a landscape, as given in Table 1. See Chapter 3 for the adjustment to soil moisture regime for different slopes.

Wetness

A measure of climatic wetness is necessary to assess soil moisture regime as well as being important in itself. Moisture deficit reflects the balance between potential evaporation and rainfall and therefore emphasises the dryness of the growing season (rather than the wetness of the winter or whole year). This biological relevance has, however, to be offset against the difficulties in calculating accurate values of evaporation. Moisture deficit is calculated by subtracting monthly rainfall from monthly evaporation and keeping a running balance throughout the summer. The peak value (in mm) reached is the moisture deficit for that year.

Previous maps for Scotland (Birse and Dry, 1970) used *potential water deficit* from long-term period mean values of monthly rainfall and monthly evaporation. For England and Wales actual monthly rainfall and evaporation were used to calculate *moisture deficit* for 20 successive years and the maps presented the mean of the 20 annual values (Bendelow and Hartnup, 1980). This method takes some account of annual variations, but is still dependent on the accuracy of the evaporation values, which up to 1975 was still not very good.

Table 1 Adjustments to accumulated temperature above $5^{\circ}C$ (AT5) for different types of slope

Gradient (degrees)	Aspect	Adjustment to AT5 (day-degrees)	Type of slope
>10	SE–S–W	Add 50	Sunny slopes
<10	All aspects	None	Neutral slopes
All gradients	W–NW	None	
All gradients	E–SE	None	
>10	NW–N–E	Subtract 50	Moderately shaded slopes
>20	NW–N–E	Subtract 100	Very shaded slopes

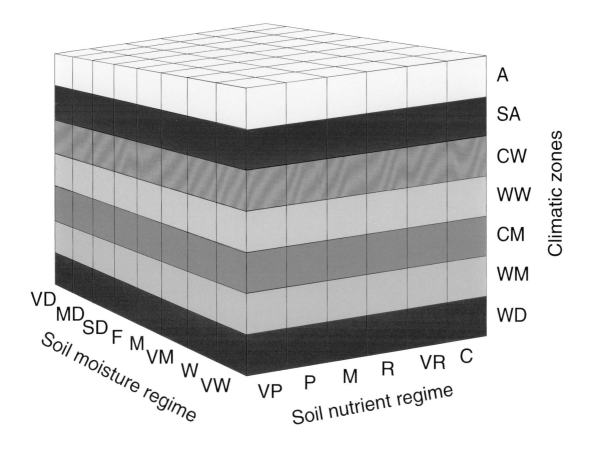

VD = Very Dry, MD = Moderately Dry, SD = Slightly Dry, F = Fresh, M = Moist, VM = Wet, VW = Very Wet.

VP = Very Poor, P = Poor, M = Medium, R = Rich, VR = Very Rich, C = Carbonate.

A = Alpine, SA = Sub-alpine, CW = Cool Wet, WW = Warm Wet, CM = Cool Moist, WM = Warm Moist, WD = Warm Dry.

Figure 1   The three 'principal components' of ecological site classification.

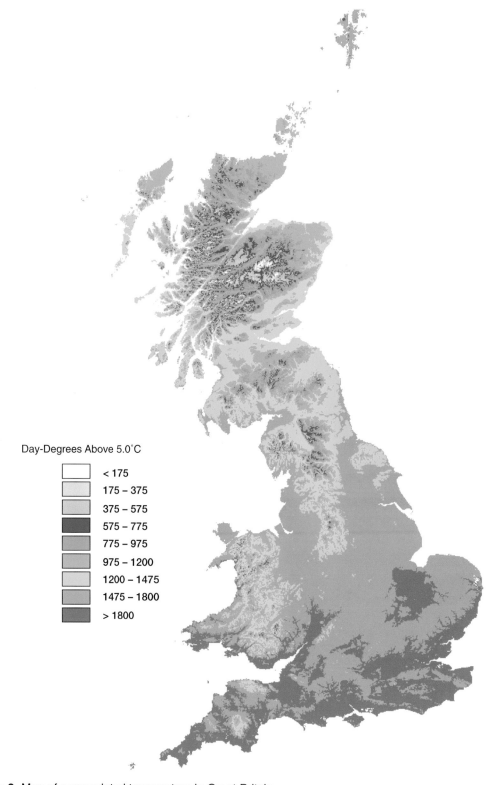

Day-Degrees Above 5.0°C

	< 175
	175 – 375
	375 – 575
	575 – 775
	775 – 975
	975 – 1200
	1200 – 1475
	1475 – 1800
	> 1800

Figure 2 Map of accumulated temperature in Great Britain.

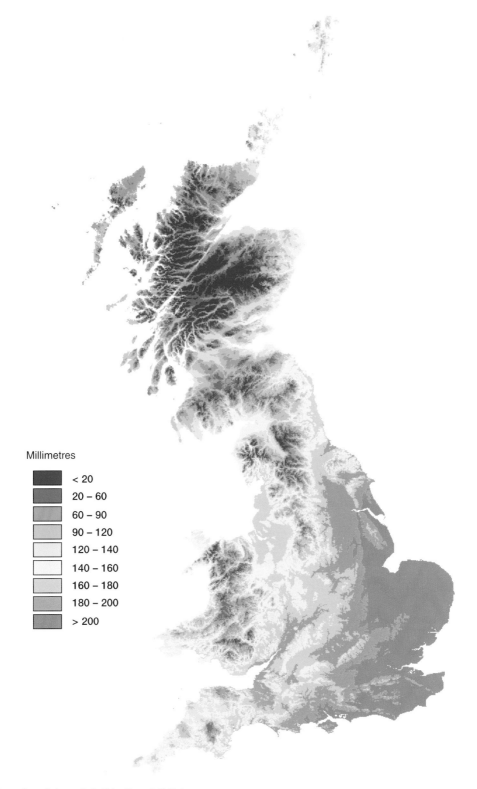

Millimetres

- < 20
- 20 – 60
- 60 – 90
- 90 – 120
- 120 – 140
- 140 – 160
- 160 – 180
- 180 – 200
- > 200

Figure 3 Map of moisture deficit in Great Britain.

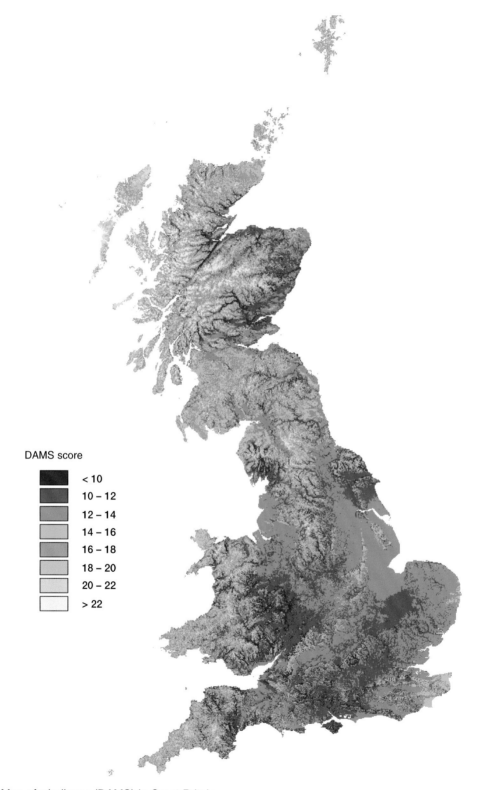

DAMS score

- < 10
- 10 – 12
- 12 – 14
- 14 – 16
- 16 – 18
- 18 – 20
- 20 – 22
- > 22

Figure 4 Map of windiness (DAMS) in Great Britain.

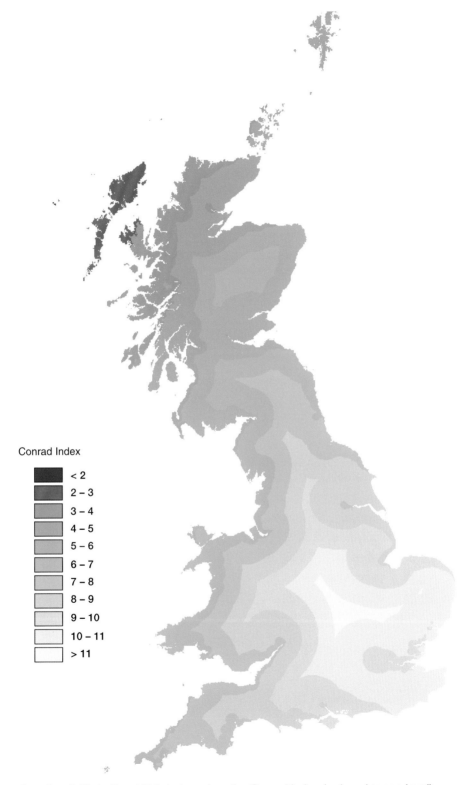

Figure 5 Map of continentality in Great Britain based on the Conrad index (reduced to sea level).

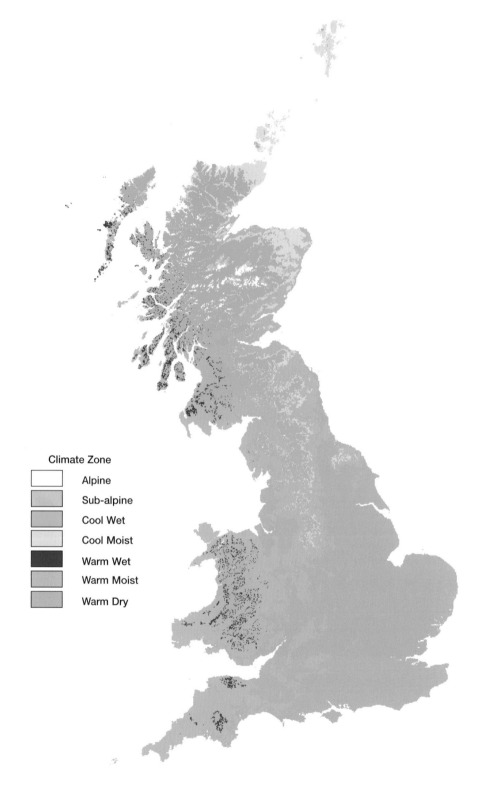

Figure 6 Map of climatic zones in Great Britain based on accumulated temperature and moisture deficit.

Climate Zone

Alpine

Sub-alpine

Cool Wet

Cool Moist

Warm Wet

Warm Moist

Warm Dry

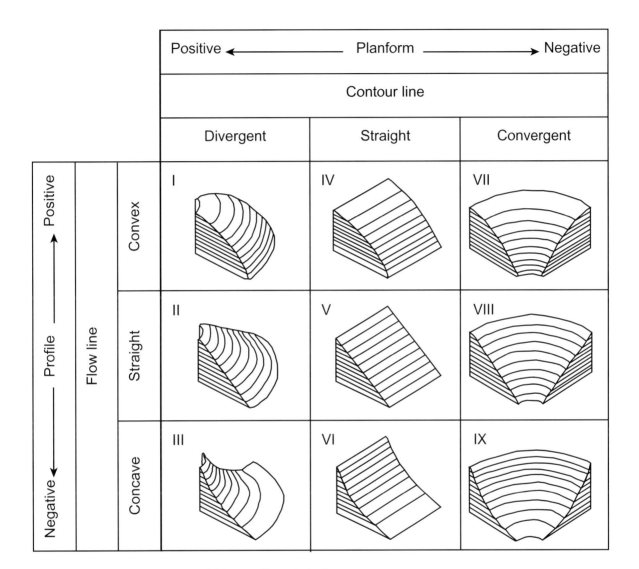

Figure 7 Nine slope shapes combining profile and planform.

	Soil nutrient regime					
	Very Poor	Poor	Medium	Rich	Very Rich	Carbonate
Humus form	mor	mor, moder	moder, oligomull	oligomull, eumull	eumull	eumull

Soil moisture regime		Soil nutrient regime					
	Very Dry	Rankers and shingle					
	Mod. Dry	Gravelly or sandy podzols and ironpan soils	Gravelly or sandy brown earths				Rendzinas
	Sl. Dry				Loamy brown earths of high base status	Calc-areous brown earths	
	Fresh	Loamy podzols and ironpan soils	Loamy brown earths				
	Moist	Podzolic gleys and peaty ironpan soils	Brown gleys		Brown gleys of high base status	Calc. brown gleys	
	V. Moist		Surface-water gleys		Surface-water gleys of high base status	Calc. surface-water gleys	
	Wet	Unflushed peaty gleys and deep peats	Flushed peaty gleys and deep peats		Humic gleys of high base status and fen peats		
	Very Wet						

Forest soil types are listed in full in Appendix 4.

Figure 8 Simplified distribution of soil types and humus forms on the soil quality grid.

Since 1975 the Meteorological Office MORECS system (Thompson *et al.*, 1981) has provided more accurate values for evaporation. Moisture deficit data for 40 x 40 km squares throughout Britain for each year of the period 1961–90 were used and the mean calculated for each square. The data were interpolated to 100 m resolution using a method similar to that used for accumulated temperature, although with only 200 squares available the precision of the interpolation formula was lower than for accumulated temperature.

The interpolation formula accounts for moisture deficit decreasing with elevation and northing but increasing with easting. Moisture deficit is not affected by distance from sea. The range of moisture deficit values in Britain is from 0 to 240 mm and is divided into nine classes grouped into 'dry', 'moist' and 'wet' zones (Figure 3).

The following two factors refine the assessment of the climate within each zone and are relevant to choice of species and timber yield.

Windiness

Windiness is the term used here to represent the amount of physiologically or physically damaging wind that a forest stand on a particular site experiences in the year. Windiness is the most likely limiting factor to tree growth at the higher elevations and near many of the coasts of Britain. The 'DAMS' (detailed aspect method of scoring) was developed by Quine and White (1993, 1994) to interpolate tatter flag data and has been found to give a good representation of both mean wind speed and the frequency of strong winds (Quine, 2000). A complete set of values at a resolution of 100 x 100 m for Britain has been calculated and the ESC-DSS selects the value for a particular grid reference from the dataset.

The formula used to calculate DAMS is based on trends of increased windiness towards the north-west of the country, near to the coasts, with increased elevation, lack of topographic shelter and on slopes open to the prevailing westerly winds (Figure 4). The range of DAMS scores is from 3 to 36 and has been divided into nine classes.

Continentality

Continentality, or its converse oceanicity, expresses the seasonal variability of the climate. Oceanic climates have a small annual range of temperature and evenly distributed precipitation. Continental climates have a large range of temperature and a summer peak of precipitation. Continentality is related to several other aspects of climate including length and intensity of the growing season, atmospheric humidity, minimum temperature and windiness. At the scale of Europe the importance of continentality is undeniable but in Britain's maritime climate the range and importance is relatively small. Nevertheless, the distribution of many plants and several of the plant communities of the National Vegetation Classification seems to be related to continentality, even after other climatic and soil factors are taken into account.

Climatologists have developed several alternative indexes of continentality, but all use the annual range of temperature as the main component. The Conrad Index is used here, following Birse (1971) and Bendelow and Hartnup (1980). The index increases with elevation, with easting and with distance from sea but decreases with northing. To simplify the map the influence of elevation has been ignored and an interpolation formula adopted that accounts for the trends with northing, easting and distance from sea. In effect, the map (Figure 5) represents continentality reduced to zero elevation. The range of values in Britain is from 1 to 13. Although twelve classes are shown on the map, for practical purposes these are grouped into four classes.

Winter cold, unseasonable frosts and other winter hazards

Occasionally, severe winters cause deaths of tree species or some provenances susceptible to extremely low temperatures by British standards. The killing temperature depends on the tree species, but a few species are susceptible to temperatures of -10°C and rather more to -20°C. In the lowlands such winters may only occur at intervals of 20 years, but even with 'global warming' there is reason to suppose that damaging winters will recur. Extreme temperatures normally occur during sustained periods of cold weather in December, January or February. Serious damage to trees can be caused by much less extreme frosts if they occur outside the dormant season. Such 'unseasonable frosts' are unpredictable as to timing and may occur anywhere in the country but are more frequent in certain topographic conditions such as 'frost hollows'.

It is not yet possible to provide a satisfactory map either of extreme winter temperature or of unseasonable frost for the requirements of ESC. In the meantime, the ESC-DSS provides broad-brush advice on the use of sensitive species such as rauli *(Nothofagus nervosa)* and the Oregon and Washington origins of Sitka spruce.

Heavy snow or ice storms occasionally cause breakage of branches or even stems of trees at any age. Although such events are unpredictable they are more frequent in the north of the country and at higher elevations. Certain races of Scots pine and provenances of lodgepole pine are particularly susceptible to snow damage, otherwise choice of species does not appear to be constrained by this risk.

Climatic zones

The four zones of warmth and the three zones of wetness are combined (Table 2) to define seven climatic zones: Warm dry, Warm moist, Warm wet, Cool moist, Cool wet, Sub-alpine and Alpine (Figure 6). The climatic zones are useful for general descriptive purposes, e.g. for describing species suitability, although we may need to subdivide a zone for greater precision. For most practical interpretations, however, the precise values for each climatic factor as calculated using the ESC-DSS will be used directly, e.g. for predicting yield class, regardless of the climatic zone the site is in.

Table 2 Definition of climatic zones in Great Britain by accumulated temperature and moisture deficit. (Shading indicates combinations not present)

Moisture deficit (mm)	Accumulated temperature (day-degrees above 5.0°C)								
	>1800	1800–1475	1475–1200	1200–975	975–775	775–575	575–375	375–175	<175
> 200	Warm Dry								
180–200									
160–180									
140–160	Warm Moist								
120–140			Cool Moist						
90–120									
60–90	Warm Wet								
20–60			Cool Wet						
<20						Sub-Alpine	Alpine		

6

The area of each climatic zone is given in Table 3.

Table 3 Area of climatic zones in Great Britain

Zone	Area (M ha)	% of total
Alpine	0.12	0.5
Sub-alpine	0.33	1.4
Cool Wet	4.60	19.8
Cool Moist	1.49	6.4
Warm Wet	0.49	2.1
Warm Moist	7.41	31.9
Warm Dry	8.79	37.9
Total	23.23	100.0

The area of individual sub-zones is shown in Table 4.

Table 4 Area of climatic sub-zones based on accumulated temperature and moisture deficit (km^2). (Shading indicates combinations not present in Britain)

Moisture deficit (mm)	Accumulated temperature (day-degrees above 5.0°C)								
	>1800	1800–1475	1475–1200	1200–975	975–775	775–575	575–375	375–175	<175
>200	18142	14146							
180–200	8221	16462							
160–180	6459	23520	910						
140–160	5180	15268	6470	78	449				
120–140	1544	9388	13127	2917	762				
90–120	48	3247	19835	10360	282	11			
60–90		2	4896	17747	2554	18			
20–60			2	5034	11676	885	<1		
<20				2	1908	6175	3258	1012	223

Chapter 3
Soil moisture regime

Introduction: moisture and oxygen availability

Soil moisture is an essential requirement for plant growth but in the forest is rarely available in exactly the right amounts at all times. Soil moisture regime expresses the availability or excess of soil moisture, with its variation throughout the year. Soil moisture regime also implicitly encompasses soil aeration, in particular the availability of oxygen for the respiration of roots and soil biota. There are eight classes within ESC: Very Dry, Moderately Dry, Slightly Dry, Fresh, Moist, Very Moist, Wet and Very Wet. These cover the wide range from permanently waterlogged soils to soils that are almost too shallow or dry for tree growth.

Classes of soil moisture regime from Very Dry to Fresh have good aeration, in that the soils are never waterlogged for periods long enough to cause oxygen concentrations to fall to levels critical for root function. In contrast, rainfall is normally insufficient during the growing season to replenish the water taken up by roots and therefore a 'soil moisture deficit' builds up. Eventually the soil becomes so dry that the roots cannot absorb all the water they need and the trees suffer from drought. The severity of the drought is mitigated by the soil's capacity to store water and release it to the roots, which are capable of growing during the drought. Therefore, these classes of soil moisture regime are defined by a combination of the (climatic) moisture deficit and the soil's available water capacity (see page 9 'Direct assessment of soil moisture regime in summer'). Tree species differ markedly in their ability to resist drought and this is taken into account in the species suitability ratings (see Figure 13).

Within the Moist to Very Wet classes of moisture regime the main problem for trees is caused by waterlogging at some depth leading to impaired aeration critical for root growth. Along the scale from Moist to Very Wet the periods of waterlogging not only become longer but the layer of inadequately aerated soil extends nearer the surface. The depth of the permanent root system of the tree is restricted and this depth, as observable in windthrown trees, can serve as the simplest definition of moisture regime. A close relationship exists between the mean depth of the water-table in winter and the rooting depth (Ray and Nicoll, 1994).

The moisture regime of ironpan soils is difficult to define, because these soils periodically have a 'perched' water-table overlying subsoil with better aeration (Pyatt and Smith, 1983). Such conditions, while common under moorland vegetation, are unlikely to persist under woodland because trees eventually develop roots which penetrate the ironpan. Interception of rainfall by the tree canopy contributes to the elimination of the perched water-table and the gradual dissolution of the ironpan.

Factors affecting soil moisture regime

Soil moisture regime is influenced by climatic, topographic and edaphic (soil) conditions. In ESC, climatic wetness is expressed by moisture deficit. As moisture deficit increases so the likelihood increases that soil moisture regime will be in the Dry classes. Conversely, in low moisture deficits it is unlikely that even freely draining soils will be drier than Fresh. The topographic influences on soil moisture regime include the position on slope (i.e. ridge crest, upper slope, midslope, footslope) and the shape of the slope (i.e. convex or shedding, straight, concave or receiving). The shape of a slope should be considered in two dimensions, across the contours and also along the contours (Figure 7).

Assessment of soil moisture regime

Direct effects of soil properties on moisture regime are mediated through soil permeability and available water capacity. These are in turn influenced by stoniness and texture, structure and depth.

The remainder of this chapter describes methods for the direct assessment of soil moisture regime; indirect methods are given in Chapters 5 and 6.

Direct assessment of soil moisture regime in winter

'Wetness class' is a scheme adopted by the National Soil Surveys (Hodgson, 1974) for describing the duration of wet states in the soil. A simplified scheme is presented in Table 5 together with an approximate equivalent depth to the winter water-table. Information on wetness class of National soil series is available in Soil Survey publications but maps have not been published. The information in Soil Survey publications has been used to predict soil moisture regimes for the major soil series in the ESC-DSS but these do not take into account the moisture deficit, topographic or local soil properties of particular sites.

The simplest way of assessing the soil moisture regime is to observe the depth to the water-table particularly in the 'winter' (normally October to March) when the water-table is likely to be at its shallowest. Some allowance should be made for exceptional weather and time must be allowed for the soil pit to equilibrate with the surrounding soil. It is also possible to relate the mean depth to the winter water-table to the degree of mottling or pale grey coloration caused by gleying. Gleying symptoms will normally occur well above the mean depth to the winter water-table, sometimes by more than 50 cm. Soils in classes Very Wet, Wet and even Very Moist will be gleyed to the surface, although this will often be masked by organic matter in the topsoil. Gleying is not visible in peat, although the smell will usually indicate the state of the aeration.

Direct assessment of soil moisture regime in summer

Soil moisture regime classes Very Dry to Slightly Dry all fall within wetness class I and rooting depths are unlikely to be restricted by the water-table. These classes are therefore additionally defined by their *droughtiness*. Droughtiness depends on the balance between the available water capacity and the dryness of the climate (the moisture deficit) as in Table 6. Droughtiness is not a problem for trees on moisture classes Fresh to Very Wet because their root systems have access to the water-table. This classification is a simplified version of a scheme used by the National Soil Surveys (Hodgson, 1974).

Adjustment of soil moisture regime for available water capacity

The available water capacity of a soil depends mainly on the texture, organic matter content, stoniness and rootable depth and is estimated using Figure 37 in Appendix 1. The method is a simplification of that described by Hodgson (1974) and Hall *et al.* (1977), but allows for the sub-division of the rooting zone according to rooting density. The most critical part of the estimate is usually estimating the depth of rooting (see page 11).

Adjustment of soil moisture regime for soil texture and stoniness

Soil texture describes the proportions of the different size fractions of particles that make up the soil. These *sand*, *silt* and *clay-sized* particles are often bound together in discrete units to give different kinds of soil structure, including crumb, blocky and prismatic shapes. Organic matter is not strictly part of soil texture, but it modifies the 'feel' of the soil and thereby the subjective assessment of soil texture.

Two methods for the assessment of soil texture are provided in Appendix 1. ESC uses broad classes of soil texture (organic, sandy, coarse loamy, fine loamy and clayey) and an estimate of the proportion of stones. The broad classes of soil texture and their finer divisions are shown in Figure 31.

Table 5 A comparison of soil moisture regime and wetness class[1]

Soil moisture class	Wetness class	Duration of wet states[2]	Winter water-table[4]
Very Dry–Slightly Dry	I	The soil profile is not wet within 70 cm depth for more than 30 days in most[3] years.	>100
Fresh	II	The soil profile is wet within 70 cm depth for 30–90 days in most years.	80–100
Moist	III	The soil profile is wet within 70 cm depth for 90–180 days in most years.	60–80
Very Moist	IV	The soil profile is wet within 70 cm depth for more than 180 days, but not wet within 40 cm depth for more than 180 days in most years.	40–60
Wet	V	The soil profile is wet within 40 cm depth for more than 180 days, and is usually wet within 70 cm for more than 335 days in most years.	20–40
Very Wet	VI	The soil profile is wet within 40 cm depth for more than 335 days in most years.	<20

[1] After Hodgson (1974) or Robson and Thomasson (1977). [2] The number of days specified is not necessarily a continuous period. [3] 'In most years' is defined as more than 15 out of 30 years. [4] Approximate mean depth (cm) to the water-table between October to March inclusive.

Table 6 Using moisture deficit and available water capacity to assess the soil moisture regime of freely draining soils

Available water capacity (mm)	Moisture deficit (mm)								
	< 20	20–60	60–90	90–120	120–140	140–160	160–180	180–200	> 200
<50	SD	SD	MD	MD- VD	VD	VD	VD	VD	VD
50–100	F	SD	SD–MD	MD	VD	VD	VD	VD	VD
100–150	F	F	F–SD	SD	MD	MD	VD	VD	VD
150–200	F	F	F	F	F–SD	SD	SD–MD	MD	MD
>200	F	F	F	F	F	F	SD	SD	SD–MD

VD = Very Dry, MD = Moderately Dry, SD = Slightly Dry, F= Fresh.

Adjustment of soil moisture regime for rooting depth

Estimating rooting depth is often difficult but nevertheless important. Opportunity may be provided by windthrown trees to build up a direct local conversion from soil type to rooting depth. Only by this kind of observation is it possible to be sure, for example, that, even without cultivation, roots can penetrate an ironpan or a compact or very stony subsoil layer or how far roots penetrate horizons with gleying symptoms. In freely draining soils that are not underlain by hard bedrock it is difficult to observe rooting depth because trees are rarely windthrown. In such circumstances, especially in lowland Britain where moisture deficits are large, it is reasonable to assume that the rooting depth is 1–1.5 m. On sandy soils a figure of 2 m would be appropriate. The zone from which a tree is able to take up moisture will always exceed the depth of roots or attached soil lifted out when the tree is uprooted.

The water-holding capacity of organic material is so high that it is important to do a separate calculation for the humus layer whenever it is thicker than a few centimetres.

Adjustment of soil moisture regime for aspect and slope

Slopes facing the sun are drier (and warmer) than shaded slopes and this is expressed in soil development. Brown earths extend to higher elevation on sunny slopes than shaded slopes and, conversely, ironpan soils occur to lower elevations on shaded slopes than on sunny slopes. Detailed data on soil moisture differences on different slopes are few, so the following are practical approximations. Table 7 defines 'sunny', 'shaded' and 'neutral' slopes and provides final adjustments for soil moisture regime classes Very Dry, Moderately Dry, Slightly Dry, Fresh and Moist (as determined by available water capacity and moisture deficit). Wetter classes do not need adjustment.

Table 7 Adjustments to soil moisture regime for different types of slope

Gradient (degrees)	Aspect	Adjustment to SMR	Type of slope
>10	SE–S–W	A half class drier	Sunny slopes
<10	All aspects	None	Neutral slopes
All gradients	W–NW	None	
All gradients	E–SE	None	
>10	NW–N–E	A half class moister	Moderately shaded slopes
>20	NW–N–E	One class moister	Very shaded slopes

Chapter 4
Soil nutrient regime

Introduction: nutrient availability

Soil nutrient regime expresses the availability of soil nutrients for plant growth. The most important soil nutrients are nitrogen (N), phosphorus (P), potassium (K), calcium (Ca) and magnesium (Mg). Other elements, including sulphur (S) and those often referred to as 'micronutrients' that are needed in smaller quantities, are rarely deficient in British forest soils (Binns *et al.*, 1980). The acidity (measured as pH) of the soil is also important as the solubility and availability for plant uptake of most nutrients is dependent upon the acidity of the soil water. In ESC the gradient of soil nutrient regime is arbitrarily divided into six classes: Very Poor, Poor, Medium, Rich, Very Rich and Carbonate.

Nitrogen is mainly taken up by plants in so-called mineral form, either as ammonium (NH_4) or nitrate (NO_3) ions, although recent research suggests that some plants can also take up amino acids. Most plants seem to take up both forms of mineral N but some plants have a preference for soils that supply most of the N in either the NH_4 or NO_3 form. There are relatively few examples of plants that prefer NH_4-nitrogen, including several ericaceous species, whereas those that prefer NO_3-nitrogen, the so-called nitrophiles, include many of the species found on Very Rich soil nutrient regimes (Ellenberg, 1988, p.129). Strongly acid soils, including many peats, tend to provide mineral N in the NH_4 form only, because the nitrification process whereby NH_4-nitrogen is converted to NO_3-nitrogen is blocked. At the other extreme, in Very Rich soils, NH_4-nitrogen released from the decomposition of organic matter is rapidly nitrified and most of the mineral N exists in the NO_3 form (Wilson, 1998).

Factors affecting nutrient availability and their potential modification

It is possible for soils to have adequate quantities of all nutrient elements except one or two. In Britain P is the element most likely to be deficient, especially in very sandy or peaty soils. It has often been necessary to 'prime' the soil with an application of P in order for tree growth to reflect properly the availability of the other nutrients and permit productive forestry (Taylor, 1991). The application of P fertilizer dramatically improves the soil nutrient regime and has a long-term effect. Such modifications may not be necessary when re-creating native woodlands.

The supply of N varies greatly in British forest soils. At one extreme the lack of N can be the main limiting factor in the soil, as in some podzolic or raw sandy soils with little organic matter. Nitrogen fertilizer can be applied to such soils but the effect may last only three years. Many strongly acid, peaty soils contain a large quantity of N but only a small proportion is available for uptake. The availability of the N in the peat can be enhanced by increasing the pH or the P supply. Increasing the pH is a difficult and expensive process and is rarely attempted, whereas the application of P to such peats is commonplace. The availability of N on infertile soils is often complicated by the presence of competitive weeds of the ericaceous family, especially heather and usually improves when such weeds are controlled or shaded out (Taylor and Tabbush, 1990).

On the deeper peat soils K may be in short supply. This tends to be linked to certain underlying lithologies and to areas well away from the influence of the sea. Elements that are supplied in significant quantities in precipitation include sodium, chlorine, K, Ca, Mg and N, but (importantly) not P. K deficiency in peaty soils is normally dealt with at the same time as P deficiency through the application of PK fertilizer.

Some acid siliceous soils have only small quantities of Ca or Mg. Concerns have been raised about the long-term supplies of these elements but to date there have not been any problems in forest stands.

It is also possible for soils to have excessive quantities of one nutrient, thereby impairing the uptake of one or more others. An example might be Ca in shallow soils derived from chalk, where the pH of the topsoil is over 7.5. Such soils, falling within the definition of the Carbonate class of nutrient regime, tend to have problems of plant uptake of P, N, K and some of the micronutrients. It is not possible to cure all of the nutrient problems of these soils and the best solution is either to plant one of the few tolerant tree species or to leave such sites unplanted. Another example of an excessive nutrient supply is given by the soils developed directly on serpentine rocks rich in Mg, but these are rare in Britain.

Wilson *et al.* (1998) showed that the most important variables in soil nutrient regime are soil pH and NO_3-nitrogen. The other major nutrients, Ca, Mg, K and P generally increase from the Very Poor class to the Very Rich class, but not necessarily at the same rate. Thus within any one class of soil nutrient regime, e.g. Medium, it is possible to have soils with relatively high levels of pH or of two or three nutrients and relatively low levels of the others. The work also showed that NH_4-nitrogen, the total amount of nitrogen (including organic forms) or the quantity of organic matter itself were not strongly involved in soil nutrient regime as a whole. It is possible, however, that the importance of NH_4-nitrogen in

very acid soils may be under-estimated, because Wilson *et al.* (1998) sampled few such soils. The Carbonate class of soils was not sampled at all, hence our knowledge of this class is based on previous work, e.g. Wood and Nimmo (1962).

Assessment of soil nutrient regime

The remainder of this chapter describes methods for the direct assessment of soil nutrient regime; indirect methods are given in Chapters 5 and 6.

Direct assessment of soil nutrient regime

Direct assessment of nutrient regime requires multiple core sampling of the soil to a depth of at least 25 cm. The amount of work involved would normally only be justified for research purposes.

The main properties of the six classes are given in Table 8. The pH of the soil is most useful for distinguishing the Carbonate, Very Rich and, to a lesser extent, the Rich class from the others. The Very Poor, Poor and Medium classes show little difference in their pH ranges. For the individual nutrients, there is a great deal of overlap between adjacent classes in the quantities recorded, therefore only qualitative descriptions of the classes are given. The importance of N and (in the poorer classes) P is emphasised in Table 8.

The broad link between soil types, lithology, humus forms and soil nutrient regime is discussed in Chapter 5. The effectiveness with which ground vegetation can be used to predict soil nutrient regime without the need for soil chemical analysis is dealt with in Chapter 6.

Table 8 Some chemical properties of soil nutrient classes in relation to silviculture

	Soil nutrient regime					
	Very Poor	**Poor**	**Medium**	**Rich**	**Very Rich**	**Carbonate**
pH (H_2O) in upper 25 cm depth	3.0–4.0	3.0–4.0	3.0–5.0	3.0–5.5	4.5–7.5	7.5–8.5
P availability	low	moderate to high	usually high	high	very high	low to moderate
P fertilizer requirement*	E. likely R. possible	E. likely except for pines, R. unlikely	unlikely except for basic igneous and some shale lithologies	unlikely	none	uncertain
N availability	very low, mainly NH_4 with a little NO_3	low, mainly NH_4 with some NO_3	moderate, both NH_4 and NO_3	moderate to high, both NH_4 and NO_3	very high, mainly NO_3	moderate, mainly NO_3
N category [#]	D, C , some B	B, A	A	not applicable	not applicable	not applicable
N fertilizer requirement*	E. and R. likely for species other than pines and larches	E. and R. possible for species other than pines and larches	unlikely	none	none	uncertain
Other nutrient problems	K often deficient on peats	none likely	none likely	none likely	none likely	N,P,K and micro-nutrients (Fe, Mn) can be unavailable

* E. for woodland establishment on bare land. * R. restocking existing woodlands. # where *Calluna* present (from Taylor, 1991).

Chapter 5

Indirect assessment of soil moisture and nutrient regimes from soil type, lithology and humus form

Introduction: forest soil types and nutrient regime

Soil type gives an initial indication of the ecological potential of the site. Figure 8 shows an arrangement of the main forest soil types (see Appendix 4) on the soil quality grid, but is a simplification and only the first step in a process of prediction of soil moisture and nutrient regimes. In this chapter the relationships between soil type, lithology, humus form and soil quality are explored in more detail.

In Figure 8 the soil types are shown rather precisely in terms of soil moisture regime. In practice there will be overlap between the soil types, for example as a consequence of the improvement of bare land by drainage. Typically this will lift peats, peaty gleys and surface-water gleys up the scale by one-half to a full class. Ironpan soils likewise move up at least one class when woodland conditions are established. At the drier end of the range, Figure 8 does not allow for the full ranges of moisture deficit and available water capacity.

The spread of soil nutrient regime within soil groups is larger than shown in Figure 8. Brown earths, surface-water gleys and peaty gleys, when bare land as well as wooded sites are included, range from Very Poor to Very Rich. Podzols are usually Very Poor or Poor but a few fall into Medium. Deep peats also have a skewed distribution towards the Very Poor end of the range but examples in Rich or Very Rich seem to exist (none were sampled by Wilson, 1998). Ironpan soils are the least variable group, being restricted to Very Poor and Poor. Rendzinas, in the strict sense of being shallow and strongly calcareous, are the defining soils of the Carbonate class, but deeper and less calcareous soils seem to be invariably Very Rich.

Clearfelling a woodland often leads to a temporary 'flush' of nutrients due to an increased rate of decomposition of the humus and leaf litter (Adamson *et al.*, 1987). The regrowth of vegetation is more vigorous and contains species usually associated with more fertile conditions than were present before (see Chapter 6).

In ESC-DSS a prediction of soil moisture and nutrient regimes is provided for three alternative classifications of soil types (Forestry Commission, Soil Survey of Scotland, Soil Survey of England & Wales) in order to cater for the varying availability of maps in different parts of the country. The forest soil classification as presented in Appendix 4 is best suited for use in ESC (see also Kennedy, 2001). The 1:50 000 or 1:25 000 scale maps of the Soil Survey of England & Wales and the Soil Survey of Scotland provide a classification at the level of soil series and are useful within their limitations of scale. Such maps exist throughout lowland Scotland, for large parts of Wales, but have only a scattered distribution in England. The national coverage of maps at the scale of 1:250 000 provides a classification of 'soil associations', each of which may comprise a mosaic of disparate soil series and is usually more informative about the lithology than the soil type. The predicted moisture and nutrient regimes based on soil associations are not adequate for forest management purposes, but should be supplemented with local observations. The detailed discussion that follows is therefore confined to the forest soil types.

Local adjustment of soil moisture regime derived from soil type

Forest soil type is more reliable for predicting soil moisture for the classes Moist to Very Wet than it is for Fresh to Very Dry. For the latter a direct assessment via available water capacity and moisture deficit is required (see Chapter 3). On a local (forest) scale the differences in moisture regime between any of the soil types shown in Figure 8 may need to be shifted up or down by half a class. This reflects that, on the national scale, soil types have overlapping ranges of moisture regime.

There is an interaction between moisture and nutrient regimes, such that the driest classes are rarely richer than Medium, and the wettest sites are rarely Very Rich.

Local adjustment of soil nutrient regime derived from soil type

Inadequate sampling of sites in the Very Poor class of nutrient regime results in a lack of precision in ESC in recognising soils within this class. Until more research can be undertaken it is useful to classify sites with some cover of heather (*Calluna vulgaris*) using the method devised by Taylor (1991). This recognised four categories of nitrogen availability (fuller details are given in Appendix 6):

Category A: Sufficient N available for acceptable tree growth

Category B: N in short supply due to competition from heather

Category C: N in short supply due to slow mineralisation and competition from heather

Category D: N in short supply due to very slow mineralisation.

It is now clear that some of the variation in nutrient regime within soil types is related to the lithology of the parent material. There is no simple or precise way of describing that relationship because of the variability *within* geological strata. However, a broad grouping of lithologies helps to refine the relationship between soil type and nutrient regime. A previous grouping for nitrogen availability has been slightly modified and extended to cover lowland England (Table 9).

The procedure for recognising the nitrogen availability category involves identifying the forest soil type (Appendix 4) in Table 10 (page 18) and the nitrogen availability categories listed alongside. Where more than one category is listed, the appropriate lithology group is found in Table 9. Group I lithologies require a move of two nitrogen availability categories to the right (e.g. from A to C for soil type 4); within Group II, move one category to the right (e.g. from C to D for soil type 11b); within Group III no amendment is required. In addition, if the soil type is mineral or organo-mineral (soil group codes 1, 3, 4, 6 or 7 in Table 10) *and* the site is dominated by heather (more than 50% ground cover – equivalent to the 'ericaceous phase' mapped in Forestry Commission soil surveys) move one further category to the right. The additional step should not be applied if the soil is classified as deep peat, i.e. soil group codes 8, 9 10 or 11. When recently fire-damaged vegetation is encountered, the dominance rating given to heather will need to be adjusted to that apparent locally on the same site type where there has been enclosure and protection from fire.

The final step in assessing nutrient regime of the poorer soils is to interpret the nitrogen availability category in terms of the classes of soil nutrient regime using Table 11.

Table 9 Ranking of the main lithologies according to the likely availability of nitrogen in overlying soils (based on Taylor, 1991)

Group I	Low nitrogen availability	Geological map* formation numbers
	Torridonian sandstone	61
	Moine quartz–feldspar–granulite, quartzite and granitic gneiss	8, 9, 10, 12
	Cambrian quartzite	62
	Dalradian quartzites	17
	Lewisian gneiss	1
	Quartzose granites and granulites	34 (part only)
	Acid volcanic and intrusive rocks	41, 46, 47
	Middle/Upper Old Red Sandstone (Scotland)	77, 78
	Upper Jurassic sandstones and grits	97, 98, 99
	Carboniferous grits and sandstones	81 (part only)
Group II	**Moderate nitrogen availability**	
	Moine mica schists and semi-pelitic schists	11
	Dalradian quartzose and mica schists, slates and phyllites	18, 19, 20, 21, 23
	Granites (high feldspar, low quartz content)	34 (part only)
	Tertiary basalts	57
	Old Red Sandstone basalts, andesite and tuff	44, 48, 50
	Silurian/Ordovician greywackes, mudstones (Scotland)	70, 71, 72, 73, 74
	Lower and Middle Jurassic sediments	91, 94, 95
	Hastings Beds	102
	Tertiary sands and gravels	109
Group III	**High nitrogen availability**	
	Gabbro, dolerite, epidiorite and hornblende schist	14, 15, 26, 27, 32, 33, 35
	Lower Old Red Sandstone	75
	New Red Sandstone	85, 89, 90
	Cretaceous shales	102–106 (part only)
	Tertiary clays	107–111 (part only)
	Upper and Lower greensands	104, 105
	Carboniferous shales and basalts	53, 54, 80[†], 81 (part only) 82, 83, 84
	Silurian/Ordovician/Devonian shales	
	(Wales and south-west England)	68, 69, 70, 71, 72, 73, 74, 75, 76, 77, 78
	Limestones and chalk	24, 67, 80[‡], 86, 91-101, 106
	Cambrian/Precambrian	60, 64, 65, 66

* Reference: British Geological Survey, Geological Survey Ten Mile Map (3rd Edition *Solid*, 1979), published by the Ordnance Survey;

† refers to Scotland only;

‡ refers to England and Wales only

Notes:

1. Geological Map formation no. 34 has been subdivided into: (a) quartzose granites and granulites (Group I), (b) granites with a high feldspar and low quartz content (Group II).

2. Geological Map formation no. 81 has been subdivided into: (a) grits and sandstones (Group I), (b) shales (Group III).

3. Where soils occur over drift material, then their characteristics (in terms of nitrogen availability) will be similar to that of the solid rock from which the drift was derived.

Table 10 Main forest soil types categorised by nitrogen availability (based on Taylor, 1991)

Soil group	Code	Soil type	Category			
Brown earths	1	Typical brown earth	A			
	1d	Basic brown earth	A			
	1u	Upland brown earth	A	B		
	1z	Podzolic brown earth	A	B		
	1e	Ericaceous brown earth	A	B	C	
Podzols	3	Typical podzol		B	C	D
	3m	Hardpan podzol		B	C	D
	3p	Peaty podzol		B	C	
Ironpan soils	4b	Intergrade ironpan soil	A	B	C	
	4	Ironpan soil	A	B	C	D
	4z	Podzolic ironpan soil		B	C	D
	4p	Peaty ironpan soil	A	B	C	
Peaty gley soils	6	Peaty gley	A	B	C	D
	6z	Peaty podzolic gley		B	C	
Surface-water gley soils	7	Surface-water gley	A	B	C	
	7b	Brown gley	A			
	7z	Podzolic gley	A	B	C	
Basin bogs	8a	*Phragmites* bog	A			
	8b	*Juncus articulatus* or *acutiflorus* bog	A			
	8c	*Juncus effusus* bog	A			
	8d	*Carex* bog	A			
Flushed blanket bogs	9a	*Molinia, Myrica, Salix* bog	A			
	9b	Tussocky *Molinia* bog; *Molinia, Calluna* bog	A	B		
	9c	Tussocky *Molinia, Eriophorum vaginatum* bog		B	C	
	9d	Non-tussocky *Molinia, Eriophorum vaginatum, Trichophorum* bog		B	C	
	9e	*Trichophorum, Calluna, Eriophorum, Molinia* bog (weakly flushed)		B	C	D
Sphagnum bogs	10a	Lowland *Sphagnum* bog				D
	10b	Upland *Sphagnum* bog				D
Unflushed blanket bogs	11a	*Calluna blanket* bog			C	D
	11b	*Calluna, Eriophorum vaginatum* blanket bog			C	D
	11c	*Trichophorum, Calluna* blanket bog				D
	11d	*Eriophorum* blanket bog				D

Table 11 Interpreting nitrogen availability category in terms of soil nutrient class

Nitrogen availability category	ESC soil nutrient class	Comments (with reference to Table 14)
A (best)	Poor, occasionally Medium	Soils are usually brown earths or surface-water gleys. Plant indicators of Poor or Medium class always present. Heather has usually been promoted by land use and should not reinvade after felling.
B	Very Poor or Poor	Wide range of soils within these two classes of nutrient regime. Plant indicators of Poor class usually present. These sites are likely to upgrade to Poor class during the first rotation and heather reinvasion should not be a serious problem after that.
C	Very Poor	Soils range from the least fertile brown earths through podzols and ironpan soils to deep peats. Plant indicators of Poor class are rare or absent. The better soils (brown earths) are likely to upgrade to Poor class by the second rotation, but some heather reinvasion after clearfelling is likely.
D (worst)	Very Poor	Soils are podzols, ironpan soils and unflushed deep peats. Plant indicators of Poor class are usually absent. These sites will not upgrade to Poor class during the first rotation and low availability of nitrogen will remain a severe limitation in the second rotation.

Local adjustment of soil nutrient regime using humus form

The form of humus reflects the activity of the fauna, bacteria and fungi responsible for breakdown of organic material accumulating on or in the soil in the form of litter and dead roots. In turn, these agents of consumption and decomposition are affected by the soil physical and chemical conditions as well as by the climate. The humus is likely to be one of the most responsive features of the soil to any changes in the environment, including changes that may bring into question the sustainability of the soil. On any given soil the nature of the litter can have an appreciable influence on the thickness and form of humus, although these features may well show cyclic changes through a rotation. For example, brown earths planted with conifers that produce acid litter, e.g. pines and spruces, may see a 'deterioration' in humus type from mull to moder before there is obvious change in the ground vegetation. Nevertheless, certain broad humus forms can be a help in identifying the soil nutrient class, especially where ground vegetation is sparse due to shading, as shown in Figure 8.

Recently there has been an increasing interest in the classification of forest humus forms in Canada (Green *et al.*, 1993) and in Europe (Brethes *et al.*, 1995, Jabiol *et al.*, 1995). A key to the identification of the small number of humus forms given on Figure 8 is provided in Appendix 2 as Figure 33.

Chapter 6

Indirect assessment of soil moisture and nutrient regimes from indicator plants

Introduction: the use of indicator plants in forestry

Plants have a certain range of tolerance of soil moisture, pH, nitrate-nitrogen, as well as temperature, light and so on. This is referred to as their ecological amplitude on each scale. When growing with other plants in a community they will usually exhibit a narrower amplitude within which they can compete successfully, their 'ecological niche'. If we know the ecological preferences for the plants in a community we can make inferences about the ecological conditions at the site.

The ecological amplitude of plants is variable. Clearly, those with a smaller amplitude (e.g. dog's mercury or wavy hair-grass) are better indicators of soil quality than those with a larger amplitude (e.g. bracken or rose-bay willowherb). Because most (and probably all) plants have an ecological niche wider than one class of soil moisture or nutrient regime it follows that plants from several classes may be found growing together at any particular site. This does not invalidate the method but it does imply that only the community of plants properly reflects soil quality. Indeed, Wilson (1998) showed that a detailed quantitative assessment of the vegetation provides a reliable indication of ESC soil nutrient class (together with a less precise indication of soil moisture).

The use of indicator plants in British forestry goes back to Gilchrist (1872) who recognised that ground vegetation indicated soil suitable for planting certain trees. In Europe, Cajander (1926) used groups of plants to help identify forest types in terms of soil moisture and nutrients, but thought of these as confounded, i.e. a single axis from dry/very poor to wet/very rich. Anderson (1950) seems to have been the first to use a grid of soil moisture and nutrient classes to help describe site types in terms of a few plants. Ellenberg (1988) used larger groups of plants to define locations on a soil moisture-pH grid. In British Columbia, Klinka et al. (1989) used lists of plants to identify classes of soil moisture and nutrient regime and described the ecological conditions in which individual species occurred. Indicator plant groups are used to describe site types on a soil moisture/nutrient grid as an aid to tree species choice in Belgium (Anon., 1991a and b). More recently in Britain, Rodwell and Patterson (1994) have listed 'optimal precursor' plants indicative of ground suitable for creation of particular new native woodland communities.

The use of numerical indicator values

Ellenberg (1988) provided indicator values, in integers from 1 to 9, to describe the soil preferences of vascular plants (flowering plants and ferns) in terms of three factors. The F value is related to soil moisture, the R value is related to soil reaction or base-status and the N value is related to nutrient supply, especially nitrogen. An F, R or N value of 1 indicates a preference for, or at least a tolerance of, very low amounts, i.e. very dry, very acid or very nutrient-poor soil. A value of 9 indicates a preference for very wet, strongly calcareous or very nutrient-rich soil. Ellenberg et al. (1992) extended the list of values from vascular plants to bryophytes and lichens. Ellenberg values are available for over 1000 British plants, but the applicability of values assigned subjectively on the basis of the behaviour of the plants in Central Europe is not assured. There are also many missing values, either where Ellenberg could not assign a value or where the plant was considered to show no ecological preference. As a consequence further work has been carried out.

Indicator values directly related to ESC soil nutrient regime have been objectively derived for about 85 vascular plants growing in British woodlands (Wilson, 1998). Wilson's indicator values are based on combining vegetation and soil chemical data and are preferable to subjectively assigned values. However, the reliability of the Wilson value depends on the frequency with which the species occurred in Wilson's sample plots, and the values for only 52 species are considered reliable.

Recently, another series of indicator values 'Ellenberg indicator values for British plants' has been supplied by Hill *et al.* (1999), representing a calibration of the F, R and N values for over 1000 plants. Although the Hill-Ellenberg values are based on the vegetation composition rather than soil analysis, this series appears to be a substantial improvement on the original European values. It also fills in the missing values of the original series.

Use of indicator plants in ESC

In ESC, indicator plants are used in conjunction with soil type, lithology and humus form to refine the estimates of soil moisture and nutrient regimes.

Species groups characteristic of particular site types have not been defined, each plant is regarded as an indicator in its own right. The recommended method of use is quantitative, involving weighting indicator values by the abundance or frequency of each plant. A semi-quantitative, short-cut method is also available. In woodland conditions the methods are more effective for soil nutrient regime than for moisture regime, although on open land both regimes are reliably estimated. For reasonable accuracy of prediction at least the five most abundant plants should be identified. Where only a few species are present it is important to record their abundance.

Only vascular plants (flowering plants and ferns) can be used in the numerical methods, although mosses can be useful indicators too, and are needed to identify some of the NVC woodlands. The Ellenberg *et al.* (1992) indicator values for bryophytes and lichens cannot be used in conjunction with the values for vascular plants. Trees and shrubs can be used as indicator species

provided they are indigenous to the site.

Two series of indicator values, the Wilson and the Hill-Ellenberg, can be used for assessing nutrient regime. The Hill-Ellenberg F values can be used for moisture regime, but with reservations (see below).

Table 12 lists the 52 woodland plants for which there are reliable Wilson nutrient indicator values (Wilson, 1998). Their Hill-Ellenberg F, R and N values are also given. Table 13 lists a further 48 plants that are important nationally or regionally either in woodlands or on open ground within woodlands, with their Hill-Ellenberg values. A further 28 less common or less widespread species are included in the ESC-DSS. Note that Hill-Ellenberg indicator values exist not only for all the plants in these lists but for over 1000 other species, including introduced species. These may be be added to later versions of the ESC-DSS.

All users of ESC intending to apply indicator plant methods should become familiar with these species at all times of the year, that is whether flowering or not. Identification keys are provided in the ESC-DSS for the important grasses, sedges and ferns. Many of the plants are included in identification keys published by the Field Studies Council (1988, 1998a, 1998b). General illustrated floras, but excluding grasses, sedges, rushes and ferns, have been produced by Blamey and Grey-Wilson (1989) and Garrard and Streeter (1998). Grasses, sedges, rushes and ferns are covered by Phillips (1980) and Rose (1989).

Assessing soil moisture and nutrient regimes using indicator plants

There are two methods: the short-cut method used in the field and the more reliable, numerical method using the ESC-DSS.

Short-cut method
This method uses Table 14, an ordination of the plants from Tables 12 and 13 on the soil quality grid. Plants are placed on the soil quality grid in the approximate centre of their ecological niches. The table has been constructed using Wilson and

Table 12 Fifty two key indicator plants for using ESC in British woodlands, with Wilson and Hill-Ellenberg indicator values

Common name	Scientific name	Wilson	Hill-Ellenberg		
			F	R	N
common bent	*Agrostis capillaris*	3.15	5	4	4
bugle	*Ajuga reptans*	5.60	7	5	5
wood anemone	*Anemone nemorosa*	4.78	6	5	4
sweet vernal-grass	*Anthoxanthum odoratum*	4.39	6	4	3
lady-fern	*Athyrium filix-femina*	4.67	7	5	6
hard fern	*Blechnum spicant*	3.48	6	3	3
false-brome	*Brachypodium sylvaticum*	5.85	5	6	5
green-ribbed sedge	*Carex binervis*	1.97	6	3	2
heather	*Calluna vulgaris*	1.70	6	2	2
rosebay willowherb	*Chamerion angustifolium*	5.09	5	6	5
enchanter's nightshade	*Circaea lutetiana*	6.02	6	7	6
hazel	*Corylus avellana*	5.35	5	6	6
hawthorn	*Crataegus monogyna*	5.58	5	7	6
cocksfoot	*Dactylis glomerata*	4.83	5	7	6
tufted hair-grass	*Deschampsia cespitosa*	5.04	6	5	4
wavy hair-grass	*Deschampsia flexuosa*	2.86	5	2	3
foxglove	*Digitalis purpurea*	4.02	6	4	5
scaly male-fern	*Dryopteris affinis*	3.74	6	5	5
broad buckler-fern	*Dryopteris dilatata*	3.94	6	4	5
male-fern	*Dryopteris filix-mas*	5.04	6	5	5
bell heather	*Erica cinerea*	2.44	5	2	2
cleavers, goosegrass	*Galium aparine*	6.90	6	7	8
heath bedstraw	*Galium saxatile*	3.06	6	3	3
herb robert	*Geranium robertianum*	4.90	6	6	6
wood avens	*Geum urbanum*	7.05	6	7	7
ground ivy	*Glechoma hederacea*	6.39	6	7	7
ivy	*Hedera helix*	4.93	5	7	6
yorkshire fog	*Holcus lanatus*	3.94	6	6	5
creeping soft-grass	*Holcus mollis*	4.00	6	3	3
bluebell, wild hyacinth	*Hyacinthoides non-scripta*	5.18	5	5	6
holly	*Ilex aquifolium*	4.33	5	5	5
soft rush	*Juncus effusus*	4.28	7	4	4
honeysuckle	*Lonicera periclymenum*	4.32	6	5	5
great woodrush	*Luzula sylvatica*	3.27	5	4	4
common cow-wheat	*Melampyrum pratense*	4.13	5	2	3
dog's mercury	*Mercurialis perennis*	6.86	6	7	7
purple moor-grass	*Molinia caerulea*	2.75	8	3	2
wood sorrel	*Oxalis acetosella*	3.74	6	4	4
tormentil	*Potentilla erecta*	2.58	7	3	2
bracken	*Pteridium aquilinum*	3.69	5	3	3
creeping buttercup	*Ranunculus repens*	4.70	7	6	7
bramble	*Rubus fruticosus*	4.60	6	6	6
raspberry	*Rubus idaeus*	4.66	5	5	5
elder	*Sambucus nigra*	6.43	5	7	7
hedge woundwort	*Stachys sylvatica*	6.79	6	7	8
greater stitchwort	*Stellaria holostea*	4.74	5	6	6
chickweed	*Stellaria media*	4.04	5	6	7
wood sage	*Teucrium scorodonia*	4.41	4	4	3
stinging nettle	*Urtica dioica*	6.64	6	7	8
blaeberry, bilberry	*Vaccinium myrtillus*	2.70	6	2	2
germander speedwell	*Veronica chamaedrys*	5.25	5	6	5
common violet	*Viola riviniana*	3.74	5	5	4

Nomenclature follows Stace (1997).

Table 13 A further 48 indicator plants for using ESC in British woodlands, with Hill-Ellenberg indicator values

Common name	Scientific name	Hill-Ellenberg		
		F	R	N
yarrow	*Achillea millefolium*	5	6	4
ramsons, wild garlic	*Allium ursinum*	6	7	7
wild angelica	*Angelica sylvestris*	8	6	5
burdock	*Arctium minus*	4	7	5
false oat-grass	*Arrhenatherum elatius*	5	7	7
marsh marigold	*Caltha palustris*	9	6	4
wood sedge	*Carex sylvatica*	5	6	5
common mouse-ear	*Cerastium fontanum*	5	5	4
golden saxifrage	*Chrysosplenium oppositifolium*	9	5	5
creeping thistle	*Cirsium arvense*	6	7	6
marsh thistle	*Cirsium palustre*	8	5	4
spear thistle	*Cirsium vulgare*	5	6	6
pignut	*Conopodium majus*	5	5	5
broom	*Cytisus scoparius*	5	4	4
crowberry	*Empetrum nigrum*	6	2	1
common horsetail	*Equisetum arvense*	6	6	6
wood horsetail	*Equisetum sylvaticum*	8	5	5
cross-leaved heath	*Erica tetralix*	8	2	1
common cotton-grass	*Eriophorum angustifolium*	9	4	1
cotton-grass, hare's-tail	*Eriophorum vaginatum*	8	2	1
wood spurge	*Euphorbia amygdaloides*	5	6	6
sheep's fescue	*Festuca ovina*	5	4	2
red fescue	*Festuca rubra*	5	6	5
meadow-sweet	*Filipendula ulmaria*	8	6	5
common hemp-nettle	*Galeopsis tetrahit*	5	6	6
hogweed	*Heracleum sphondylium*	5	7	7
slender St John's wort	*Hypericum pulchrum*	5	4	3
sharp-flowered rush	*Juncus acutiflorus*	8	4	2
compact rush	*Juncus conglomeratus*	7	4	3
heath rush	*Juncus squarrosus*	7	2	2
yellow archangel	*Lamiastrum galeobdolon*	5	7	6
heath woodrush	*Luzula multiflora*	6	3	3
yellow pimpernel	*Lysimachia nemorum*	7	4	5
bog myrtle	*Myrica gale*	9	3	2
mat-grass	*Nardus stricta*	7	3	2
lousewort	*Pedicularis sylvatica*	8	3	2
rough meadow-grass	*Poa trivialis*	6	6	6
primrose	*Primula vulgaris*	5	6	4
lesser celandine	*Ranunculus ficaria*	6	6	6
sheep's sorrel	*Rumex acetosella*	5	4	3
red campion	*Silene dioica*	6	6	7
devil's-bit scabious	*Succisa pratensis*	7	5	2
deer-grass, deer-sedge	*Trichophorum cespitosum*	8	2	1
white clover	*Trifolium repens*	5	6	6
gorse	*Ulex europaeus*	5	5	3
cowberry	*Vaccinium vitis-idaea*	5	2	2
common valerian	*Valeriana officinalis*	8	6	5
wood speedwell	*Veronica montana*	6	6	6

Nomenclature follows Stace (1997).

Hill-Ellenberg values and is therefore of uncertain reliability. Where available, the Wilson nutrient value has been given priority over the Hill-Ellenberg R+N value. Location on the moisture axis is based on the Hill-Ellenberg F value.

In the short-cut method at least the five most abundant plants are identified and listed in order of abundance (cover percentage). The moisture and nutrient regimes of the site are judged from an informal 'weighted average' of the cells occupied by the plants on Table 14. For example if the five most abundant plants were broad buckler-fern (50%), creeping soft-grass (30%), wood sorrel (10%), bracken (10%) and tufted hair-grass (5%), the weighted average soil quality indicated would be Moist Medium.

Numerical method for assessing soil moisture regime

The Hill-Ellenberg F values could be used to calculate a weighted mean value for soil moisture in the same way as the R+N value is used for soil nutrients, but this method is not considered sufficiently precise for most woodlands. The range of values is between 5 and 6 for most commercial plantations and under-estimates the variation in moisture regime evident in the soil. This is in spite of the fact that the method works well for non-woodland vegetation and is effective at differentiating the 'wet woodlands' from the other NVC woodlands (see chapter 8). It is recommended therefore, that the use of indicator plants for soil moisture regime should be confined to the use of Table 14 as a check or refinement for the assessment made by the methods given in chapters 3 and 5.

Numerical method for assessing soil nutrient regime

This method produces a weighted average indicator value for a site from a description of the ground vegetation using the method given below. The calculation of the weighted average indicator value for a site involves, for each plant in turn, multiplying the abundance by the indicator value, summing the products and finally dividing by the sum of the abundances. The calculation is performed most easily within the ESC-DSS. The ESC-DSS calculates the weighted average indicator values and identifies the nutrient class using Table 15, having applied the rule to choose between Wilson and Hill-Ellenberg (see footnote to Table).

Method of obtaining quantitative data on indicator plants for ESC

A good description of the vegetation is obtained from 10 quadrats each 2 x 2 m in size, arranged systematically over the site. The number of quadrats may be reduced to five if the vegetation looks fairly uniform. All vascular plants (flowering plants and ferns) should be identified and their abundance recorded as a percentage. Shrubs over 1 m tall should be treated as a separate layer, otherwise bracken, ferns, grasses and herbs can be recorded in the same ('field') layer. Bryophytes are usually treated as another ('ground') layer, but for ESC purposes they can be ignored. Where the field layer is itself layered, e.g. where bracken is present, the sum of abundance values will often exceed 100 per cent. The percentages should be summed and, if necessary, each species' value adjusted to produce the appropriate total. The natural tendency is to under-estimate abundance. The 'abundance charts' attached to the soil description method (Figure 36) may be helpful. If there is a lot of bare soil present, and this is not simply the result of dense bracken, bramble or other tall plants, then the total cover will add up to less than 100 per cent. Where the total cover is less than about 10 per cent the reliability of the method is open to question, although a larger sample may be a worthwhile expedient.

A suitable form for recording the details of site and vegetation is given as Figure 35 in Appendix 3.

Table 14 Indicator plants for the short-cut method of assessment of soil moisture and nutrient regimes in British woodlands (based on Wilson, 1998 and Hill *et al.*, 1999)

		Soil nutrient regime[1]				
		Very Poor	Poor	Medium	Rich	Very Rich
Soil moisture regime	Slightly Dry			wood sage		burdock
	Fresh	cowberry, bell-heather	**wavy hair-grass, common bent, bracken, common violet, great woodrush, slender St John's wort,** sheep's sorrel, sheep's fescue	**raspberry, holly, greater stitchwort, cow-wheat, chickweed,** broom, gorse, common mouse-ear	**bluebell (wild hyacinth), hazel, ivy, hawthorn, false-brome, rosebay willowherb, germander speedwell, wood sedge, pignut, primrose,** cocksfoot, red fescue, yarrow	**elder, yellow archangel, wood spurge,** common hemp-nettle, spear thistle, white clover, false oat-grass, hogweed
	Moist	**bilberry (blaeberry),** heather, crowberry, green-ribbed sedge	**wood sorrel, scaly male-fern, hard fern, heath bedstraw,** heath woodrush	**bramble, creeping soft-grass, broad buckler-fern, wood anemone, foxglove, honeysuckle,** yorkshire fog, sweet vernal-grass	**tufted hair-grass, male-fern, herb robert**	**dog's mercury, goosegrass (cleavers), ramsons, stinging nettle, hedge woundwort, ground ivy, wood avens, enchanter's nightshade, lesser celandine, red campion, wood speedwell,** common horsetail, creeping thistle, rough meadow-grass
	Very Moist	mat-grass, tormentil, heath rush	compact rush, devil's bit scabious	**lady-fern, yellow pimpernel, creeping buttercup,** soft rush	bugle	
	Wet	**purple moor-grass,** cotton-grass (hare's-tail), cross-leaved heath, deer-grass, lousewort	sharp-flowered rush	marsh thistle	**wood horsetail, common valerian,** meadow-sweet, wild angelica	
	Very Wet	common cotton-grass, bog myrtle			**golden saxifrage,** marsh marigold	

[1] There are no common indicator plants for the Carbonate class

Shade-tolerant species are in **bold** type

Table 15 Conversion of the weighted mean indicator value for a site to the nutrient class

Nutrient class	Very Poor	Poor	Medium	Rich	Very Rich	Carbonate
Wilson nutrient indicator value	<2.8	2.8–3.9	3.9–4.8	4.8–6.0	> 6.0	no data
Hill-Ellenberg R+N value	<5.7	5.7–7.7	7.7–9.7	9.7–11.7	>11.7	R value >6.0
						N value <4.5

Rule for choosing between Wilson and Hill-Ellenberg values: Where plants with Wilson values constitute 60 per cent or more of the vegetation of a site the Wilson values are preferred. For sites where plants with Wilson values have less than 60 per cent of the vegetation cover, the Hill-Ellenberg R+N values are used (for details of the method see Chapter 8).

Chapter 7
Choice of tree species for ESC site types

Introduction: species suitability

Choice of tree species is one of the most important silvicultural decisions the manager makes and it is affected by ecological, financial and practical considerations. The advice that follows provides a list of species that are ecologically suited to particular climates and soil qualities in Britain and capable of producing good quality timber. The timber-producing capability does not, however, extend to the Sub-alpine zone and trees cannot grow at all in the Alpine zone.

Tree species suitability can be represented in three classes, *very suitable*, *suitable* and *unsuitable*. For each species the range of values of each climatic factor is divided into three sectors and labelled with these ratings (Figures 9 to 12). The classes of soil moisture regime and soil nutrient regime are rated in a similar way (Figures 13 and 14). When combining the ratings of each factor to arrive at an overall suitability for a particular site, it is the lowest rating that determines the outcome. Differences from Pyatt and Suárez (1997) reflect new climatic data and their class boundaries, and refinements of the earlier advice. The term *very suitable* is now preferred to *optimal*.

In *very suitable* conditions a tree species is expected to grow at a rate given by the upper third of the range of yield class shown in the Yield Models (Edwards and Christie, 1981) and to be capable of doing so without undue risk of disease or pest attack to an age well above that of normal financial maturity. It may thus be an appropriate species/site combination to choose for long-term retention for landscape or wildlife reasons. The species will also be capable of producing viable seed for natural regeneration (see below). In *suitable* conditions, unless limited by lack of warmth, a tree species is either expected to grow at a rate given by the middle third of the range of

yield class in the Yield Models, or it is expected to grow well early in its life but with reduced growth in the later part of the rotation. Where rate of growth is limited by lack of warmth, the species should still be capable of growing to biological maturity but natural regeneration will be unreliable. Where there are increased risks of injury from pests, disease or drought, then the species is considered incapable of growing to normal biological maturity. It should not be considered appropriate for long-term retentions. A species is considered *unsuitable* when the risks of it being incapable of producing sawlogs are too high.

It is assumed that climatic and soil factors cannot compensate for one another. Thus a *very suitable* climate cannot compensate in terms of yield for an *unsuitable* soil quality, and *vice versa*. Similarly, if any one factor, climatic or soil, is *unsuitable*, a favourable rating of any or all of the other factors cannot make the site *suitable* for the species. This does not, of course, preclude the possibility that appropriate management of a site could be used to upgrade soil quality to achieve a higher rating.

The species suitability criteria are essentially subjective and draw on personal experience in Britain and abroad, in particular British Columbia, together with a wide variety of literature. Some of the more useful literature, in alphabetical order, is as follows: Aldhous and Low, 1974; Anderson, 1950; Anon., 1991a; Anon., 1991b; Day, 1957; Evans, 1984; Franklin and Dyrness, 1973; Krajina, 1969; Lines, 1987; Macdonald, 1952; Macdonald *et al.*, 1957; Savill, 1991; Schmidt, 1957; Weissen *et al.*, 1994; Wood, 1955; Wood and Nimmo, 1962.

In the ESC-DSS the stepped changes in suitability rating have been replaced by smooth 'response curves', an example of which is given as Figure 15.

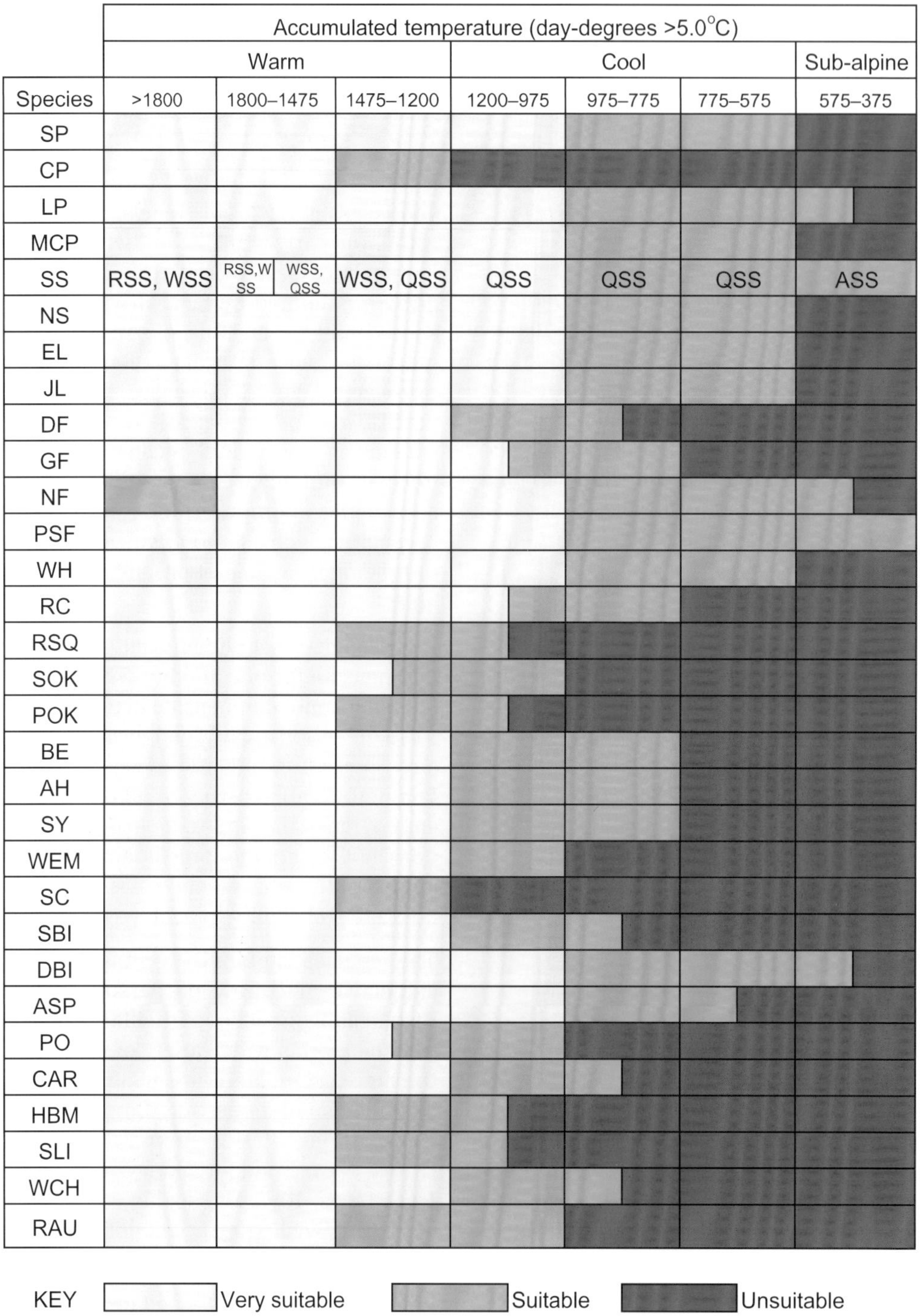

	Accumulated temperature (day-degrees >5.0°C)						
	Warm			Cool			Sub-alpine
Species	>1800	1800–1475	1475–1200	1200–975	975–775	775–575	575–375
SP							
CP							
LP							
MCP							
SS	RSS, WSS	RSS,WSS / WSS,QSS	WSS, QSS	QSS	QSS	QSS	ASS
NS							
EL							
JL							
DF							
GF							
NF							
PSF							
WH							
RC							
RSQ							
SOK							
POK							
BE							
AH							
SY							
WEM							
SC							
SBI							
DBI							
ASP							
PO							
CAR							
HBM							
SLI							
WCH							
RAU							

KEY ☐ Very suitable ▨ Suitable ▨ Unsuitable

For explanation of species abbreviations and seed origins see Appendix 6. Where seed origins are given, these are the only ones recommended.

Figure 9 Suitability of tree species by accumulated temperature.

	Moisture deficit (mm)								
	Wet			Moist			Dry		
Species	<20	20–60	60–90	90–120	120–140	140–160	160–180	180–200	>200
SP	WEST		NATIVE						
CP									
LP	COASTAL		COASTAL		KLP	KLP, CLP	KLP, CLP	CLP	CLP
MCP									
SS									
NS									
EL									
JL									
DF									
GF									
NF									
PSF									
WH									
RC									
RSQ									
SOK									
POK									
BE									
AH									
SY									
WEM									
SC									
SBI									
DBI									
ASP									
PO									
CAR									
HBM									
SLI									
WCH									
RAU									

KEY ☐ Very suitable   ▨ Suitable   ▧ Unsuitable

For explanation of species abbreviations and seed origins see Appendix 6. Where seed origins are given, these are the only ones recommended.

Figure 10 Suitability of tree species by moisture deficit.

Species	\<10	10–12	12–14	14–16	16–18	18–20	20–22	\>22
				Windiness (DAMS score)				
SP								
CP								
LP						ALP, NLP		
MCP								
SS								
NS								
EL								
JL								
DF								
GF								
NF								
PSF								
WH								
RC								
RSQ								
SOK								
POK								
BE								
AH								
SY								
WEM								
SC								
SBI								
DBI								
ASP								
PO								
CAR								
HBM								
SLI								
NOM								
WCH								
RAU								

KEY: Very suitable | Suitable | Unsuitable

For explanation of species abbreviations and seed origins see Appendix 6. Where seed origins are given, these are the only ones recommended.

Figure 11 Suitability of tree species by windiness.

Species	Continentality <5	5–7	7–9	>9
SP	▓			
CP				
LP	ALP, NLP, KLP			
MCP	▓			
SS				▓
NS	▓	▓	▓	
EL	▓			
JL				▓
DF	▓			
GF	▓			
NF	▓			▓
PSF				▓
WH				
RC				▓
RSQ				▓
SOK	▓	▓		
POK		▓	▓	
BE	▓			
AH				
SY				
WEM	▓			
SC	▓			
SBI	▓	▓		
DBI				▓
ASP				
PO				
CAR				
HBM	▓	▓	▓	
SLI	▓	▓	▓	
NOM	▓	▓	▓	
WCH	▓			
RAU				▓

KEY: (blank) Very suitable ▓ Suitable

For explanation of species abbreviations and seed origins see Appendix 6. Where seed origins are given, these are the only ones recommended.

Figure 12 Suitability of tree species by continentality.

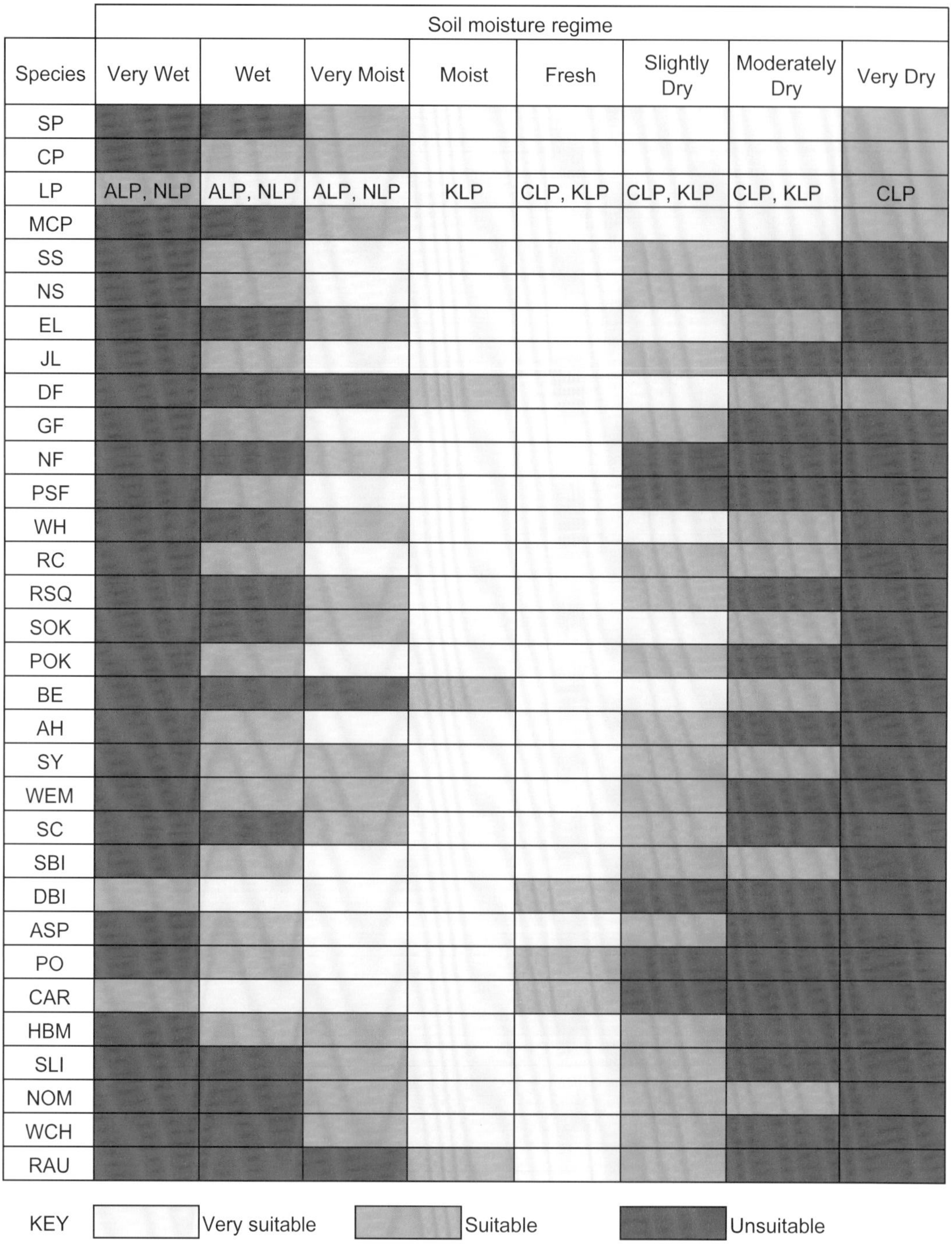

Species	\multicolumn{8}{c}{Soil moisture regime}

Species	Very Wet	Wet	Very Moist	Moist	Fresh	Slightly Dry	Moderately Dry	Very Dry
SP								
CP								
LP	ALP, NLP	ALP, NLP	ALP, NLP	KLP	CLP, KLP	CLP, KLP	CLP, KLP	CLP
MCP								
SS								
NS								
EL								
JL								
DF								
GF								
NF								
PSF								
WH								
RC								
RSQ								
SOK								
POK								
BE								
AH								
SY								
WEM								
SC								
SBI								
DBI								
ASP								
PO								
CAR								
HBM								
SLI								
NOM								
WCH								
RAU								

KEY ☐ Very suitable ☐ Suitable ☐ Unsuitable

For explanation of species abbreviations and seed origins see Appendix 6. Where seed origins are given, these are the only ones recommended.

Figure 13 Suitability of tree species by soil moisture regime.

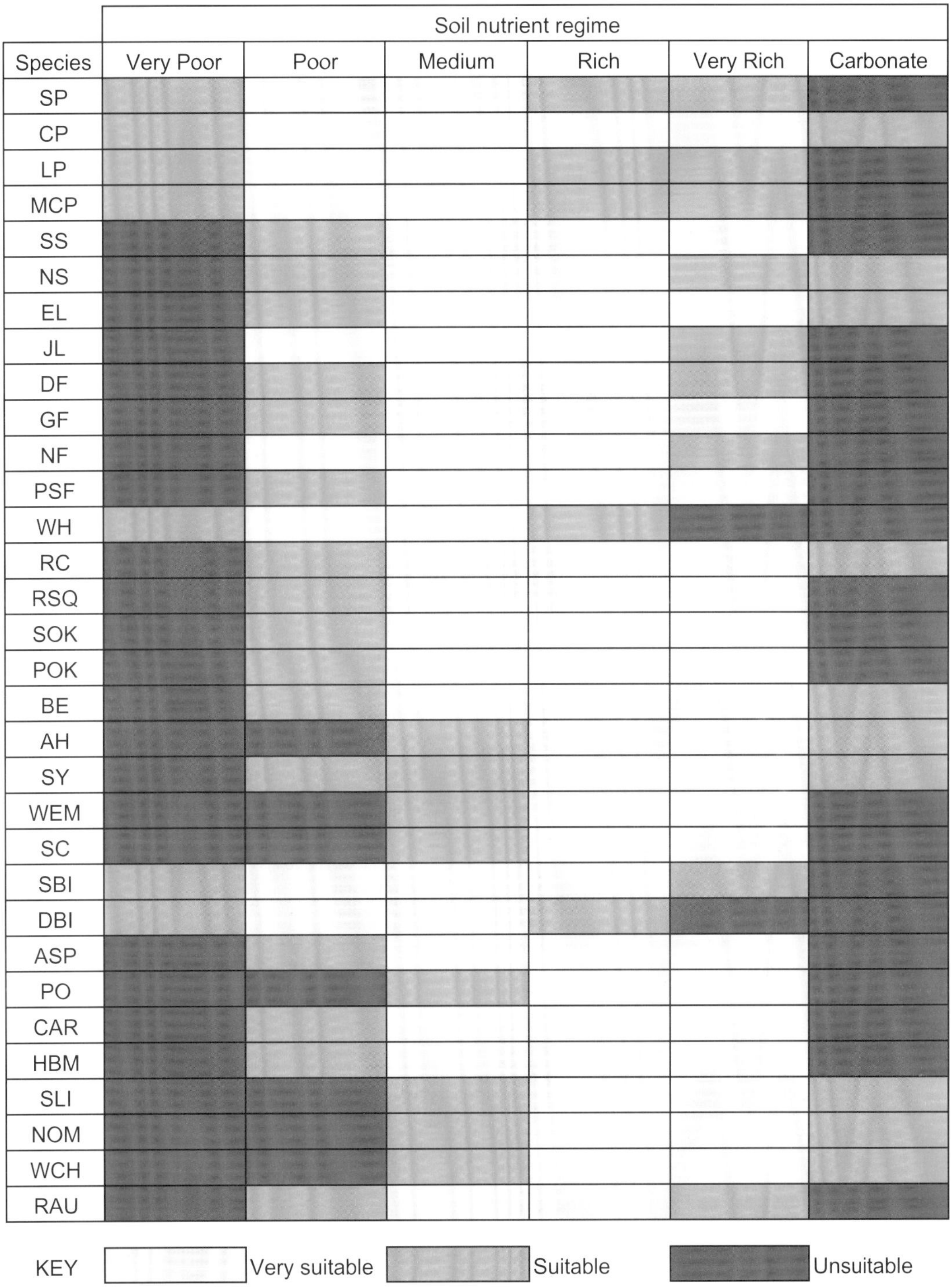

	Soil nutrient regime					
Species	Very Poor	Poor	Medium	Rich	Very Rich	Carbonate
SP						
CP						
LP						
MCP						
SS						
NS						
EL						
JL						
DF						
GF						
NF						
PSF						
WH						
RC						
RSQ						
SOK						
POK						
BE						
AH						
SY						
WEM						
SC						
SBI						
DBI						
ASP						
PO						
CAR						
HBM						
SLI						
NOM						
WCH						
RAU						

KEY: Very suitable | Suitable | Unsuitable

For explanation of species abbreviations and seed origins see Appendix 6. Where seed origins are given, these are the only ones recommended.

Figure 14 Suitability of tree species by soil nutrient regime.

The uppermost curve shows how yield class is assumed to be related to accumulated temperature, given that other conditions of climate and soil are ideal for the species (within British conditions). This is termed the 'potential yield class'. The remaining curves show how the potential yield class of the species is held to be affected by variation in the other climatic and soil factors. Here the vertical axis ranges from 0 to 1. In relation to the suitability class system, the change from *very suitable* to *suitable* usually coincides with a ratio of 0.75 and the change from *suitable* to *unsuitable* with a ratio of 0.5.

The ESC-DSS predicts yield class in the following way. For a particular site the climatic values are calculated and the classes of soil moisture and nutrient regime are determined. Each value is marked on the horizontal axes and the value of potential yield class and the values of the ratios (from the other curves) are read off. Whichever is the lowest ratio is then multiplied by the potential yield class to obtain the predicted yield class.

The method is based on the assumption that lack of warmth is generally a limiting factor to tree growth in Britain and that when other limiting factors are present it is only the most limiting factor that needs to be taken into account. The method is a departure from the traditional view that sites are a complex combination of multiple factors each of which can affect the operation of the others. The new method is relatively easy to program, but its validity remains to be proved.

Risks

In the species suitability ratings, *very suitable* site conditions of a species are equated not only with high yield class but also with low risk of pests, diseases and abiotic problems. The following site-related risks should be particularly guarded against. Species susceptible to butt-rot on Rich or Very Rich soils are: NS, EL, WH and RC. SP is susceptible to fungal defoliation in Wet climatic zones or where accumulated temperature is <775 day-degrees. Species sensitive to frost include CP, SS (when young), EL, JL, DF, GF, WH, RC, SOK, POK, BE, AH. CP and RAU are unusual in that they are liable to be killed at any age by extreme winter

cold. (A key to species abbreviations is contained in Appendix 6 'Glossary of Terms'.)

Timber quality

In *very suitable* site conditions a species is also expected to produce stems of good form and timber of good quality if managed appropriately. For some species certain climatic and soil conditions can be expected to lead to timber quality problems and should be avoided. The following species should not be planted on 'sunny slopes' (see Table 7) because of the risk of developing drought cracks in the stem: NF, PSF, GF. Coarse branching and poor stem form tends to be a problem in SP, LP, WH, SBI and DBI on Rich or Very Rich soils.

Natural regeneration

The capacity for natural regeneration of a tree or stand depends upon the production of viable seed, appropriate conditions on the forest floor for germination (the 'seedbed') and adequate light for the subsequent growth of the seedlings. The first two of these depend on site conditions that can be specified in ESC. Broadly speaking, *very suitable* site conditions are likely to lead to the production of plentiful seed once the tree has reached the necessary age. Where the climate and especially the warmth is only *suitable* for the species, production of seed may be less abundant or at longer intervals of years. The light requirements (or shade tolerance) of trees and of seedlings in particular are indicated in Figure 16, based on Hill *et al.* (1999). The shade tolerance of a few species, including ash, is somewhat higher in the seedling/sapling stages than at greater age. The most shade tolerant species, including beech and western hemlock, actually benefit from some shading in the early years, as indicated in Figure 16.

Included in 'seedbed conditions' is the competition the seedling suffers from other plants (weed growth). This again is predictable from ESC soil quality. Although more research is required on the complexity of British conditions, natural regeneration is more readily achieved where weed

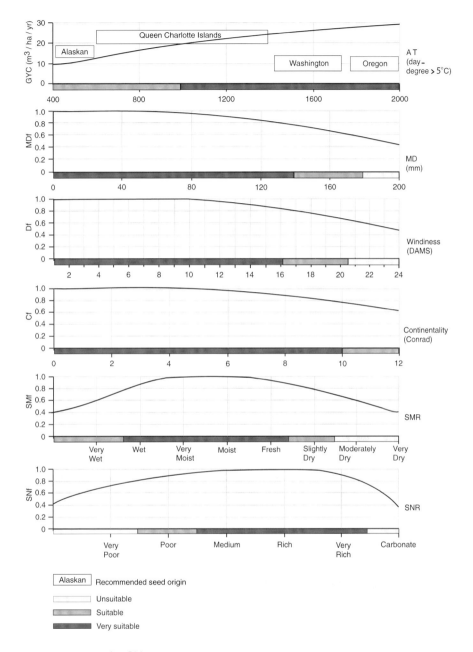

Figure 15 Smooth response curves for Sitka spruce.

growth is less strong, and this means either where the soil is less moist or poorer in nutrient supply. In other words, natural regeneration tends to occur on sites that are less than ideal for the growth (timber yield) of the species. It is difficult to achieve successful natural regeneration on sites that are either wet or rich or both (Figure 17). For greater detail see Nixon and Worrell (1999), and Harmer and Kerr (1995).

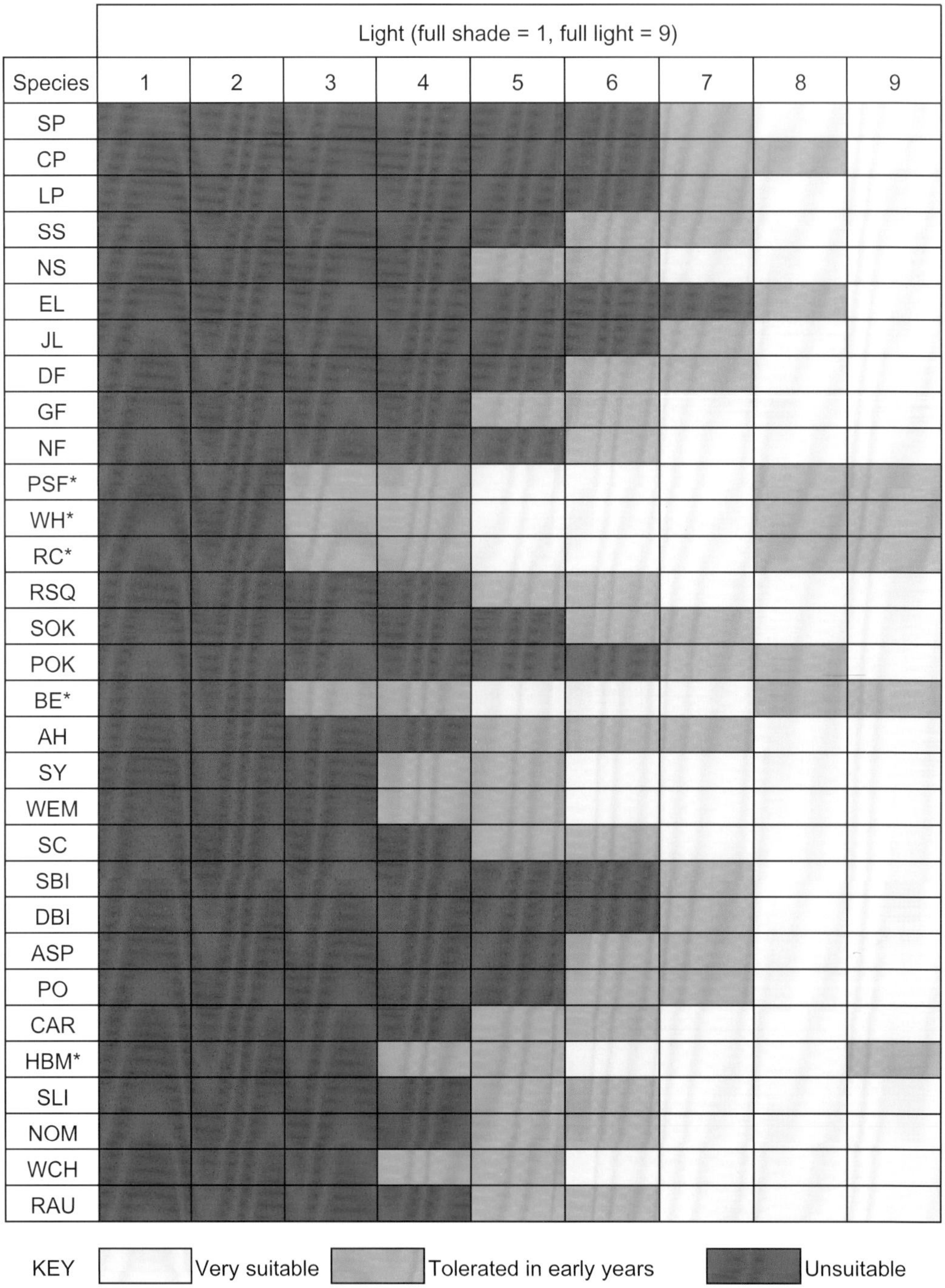

	Light (full shade = 1, full light = 9)								
Species	1	2	3	4	5	6	7	8	9
SP									
CP									
LP									
SS									
NS									
EL									
JL									
DF									
GF									
NF									
PSF*									
WH*									
RC*									
RSQ									
SOK									
POK									
BE*									
AH									
SY									
WEM									
SC									
SBI									
DBI									
ASP									
PO									
CAR									
HBM*									
SLI									
NOM									
WCH									
RAU									

KEY: Very suitable | Tolerated in early years | Unsuitable

For explanation of species abbreviations and seed origins see Appendix 6.
* For these species partial overhead cover is beneficial in the early years.

Figure 16 Relative shade tolerance of tree species in Britain (based on Hill *et al.*, 1999).

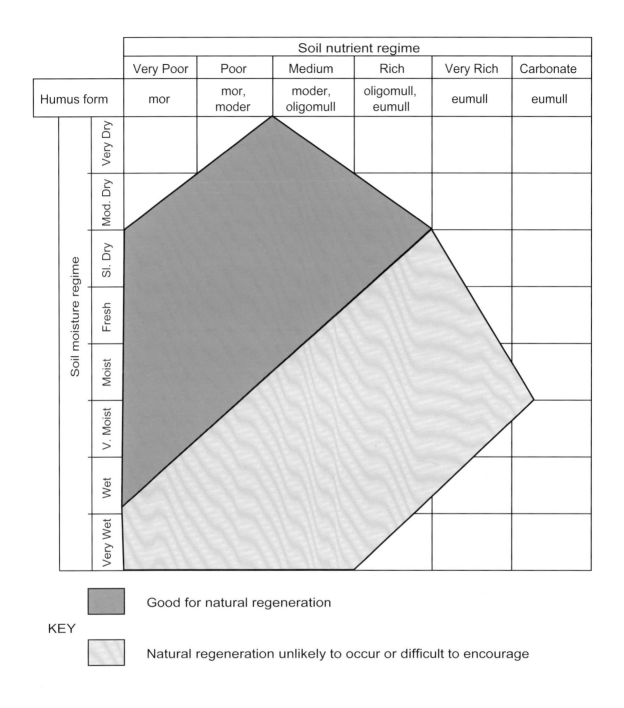

Figure 17 Soil quality and the prospects for natural regeneration of conifers (after Nixon and Worrell, 1999).

Chapter 8

Native woodlands for ESC site types

Introduction: climate and soil suitability

When new native woodland is being created the main objective is to develop natural character by using a community of locally native tree and shrub species matched to the site. Natural character means that the ground vegetation that develops beneath the trees is in harmony not only with the site but also with the composition of the overstorey. This is most likely to be achieved by using as a model the particular National Vegetation Classification (NVC) woodland sub-community that is matched to the ESC site type.

The different types of native woodland in Britain (Rodwell, 1991) are distributed in relation to site conditions, both at national and local scales. The NVC lays more emphasis on site conditions than on strict definitions of woodland 'stand types' (Peterken, 1981). As an example, the W9 ash–rowan–dog's mercury woodland is described by Rodwell (1991) as characteristic of permanently moist, base-rich brown earth soils in the uplands, yet due to natural processes and the intervention of man, can actually be an ashwood, a birchwood, an alderwood, a beechwood, an oakwood, an elmwood or even a sycamore wood. Rodwell (1991) described the distribution of woodlands in terms of three main climatic zones and three soil groups. The climatic trend is from the cooler wetter north-west to the warmer drier south-east. The soil trend is from calcareous soils through brown earths of low base-status to very acid rankers and podzolic soils.

The climatic and soil relationships with NVC woodlands are made more explicit by Whitbread and Kirby (1992) and by Rodwell and Patterson (1994). The latter include simple maps of 'upland' and 'lowland' climatic zones. It is still surprisingly difficult to visualise the differences in site quality between communities and between sub-communities within communities. However, it should be possible to find a position within the ESC 'cube of ecospace' appropriate to each NVC woodland. In practice, it is the location of the woodlands on the soil quality grid that is most interesting.

Linking native woodlands with the soil quality grid

Rodwell (1991) provided floristic lists for each woodland sub-community compiled from a number of quadrats. The proportion of the quadrats in which each plant occurred was given as the frequency in five classes (I = 1–20%, II = 21–40% and so on to V = 81–100%).

The method used here to link NVC woodlands with the soil quality grid is similar to that of Pyatt (1997) but uses the Hill-Ellenberg values (Hill *et al.*, 1999). Each plant in the floristic list of a sub-community is assigned its F, R and N value (see Chapter 6). The value is multiplied by the frequency and the resulting sum of products is divided by the sum of the frequencies. The weighted mean indicator value for F (mF) is used directly as a measure of the characteristic soil moisture regime for the sub-community. The weighted mean values for R and N are added together (mR+mN) and used as the measure of soil nutrient regime. Wilson (1998) showed that mR and mN, based on the abundance of each plant in his plots, were closely related to soil nutrient regime as determined by soil chemical analysis. Figure 18 shows the location of each NVC woodland sub-community on the soil quality grid and the main groups of woodlands (broad stand types) are delineated by boxes. The distribution of the sub-communities on the grid is discussed in detail by Pyatt (1997).

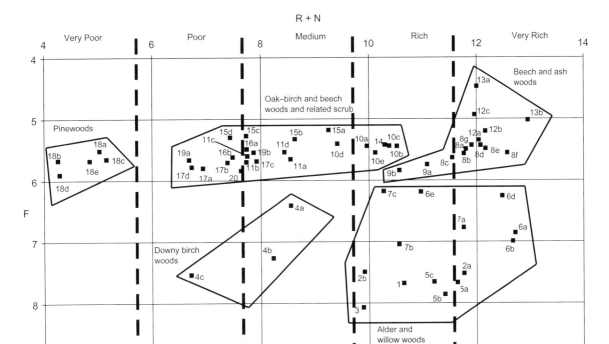

Figure 18 Ordination of NVC woodland sub-communities W1–W20 on scales of F ('soil moisture') and R+N ('soil nutrients') with approximate boundaries (broken vertical lines) of soil nutrient classes. Species indicator values from Hill *et al.,* 1999.

Separating the communities by climatic zones

Placing all the woodland sub-communities together on Figure 18 appears complicated because it does not make use of the climatic factors to separate upland and lowland communities. In practice the climatic relationships are not very precise and communities labelled 'upland' or 'lowland' by Rodwell and Patterson (1994) can occur in close geographical proximity (Hall, 1998). Nevertheless the distinction is maintained in the interests of clarity in Figures 19–22. Here only the communities are shown, the size and location of each box being based subjectively on the spread of the component sub-communities. In addition to the main lowland/upland split, two communities of scrub woodland (W19 juniper and W20 willow) are assigned to the Sub-alpine zone. For additional clarity the beechwoods and the lowland ashwoods

and oakwoods are shown on separate Figures, although their climatic zones undoubtedly overlap. The names of the woodlands given are those of Rodwell and Patterson (1994).

Suitability ranges of all six ESC site factors

The suitable range of each climatic and soil factor for all NVC woodlands W1–W20 is shown in Figures 23–28. The soil requirements of the woodlands are more critical than the climatic requirements. Where possible, the requirements of individual sub-communities are shown separately. Only two classes of suitability are given. In *suitable* conditions the woodland can be expected to regenerate itself. In *unsuitable* conditions natural regeneration of either the tree species or some of the characteristic species of the ground vegetation would not occur.

In the ESC-DSS, the method of choosing NVC woodland communities appropriate to site types uses 'smooth response curves' derived from these suitability classes in a similar way to those used for individual tree species (see Chapter 7).

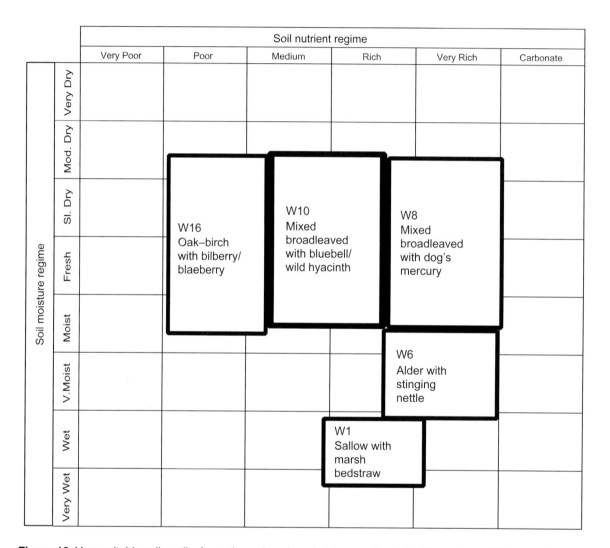

Figure 19 Very suitable soil quality for native oak, ash and alder woodlands in Warm dry and Warm moist climatic zones (the 'Lowland Zone' of FC Bulletin 112 (Rodwell and Patterson, 1994)).

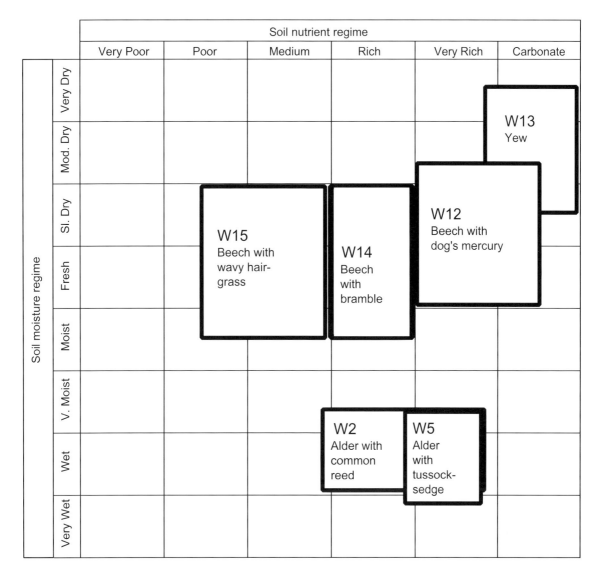

Figure 20 Very suitable soil quality for native beech woodlands in Warm dry and Warm moist climatic zones (the 'Lowland Zone' of FC Bulletin 112).

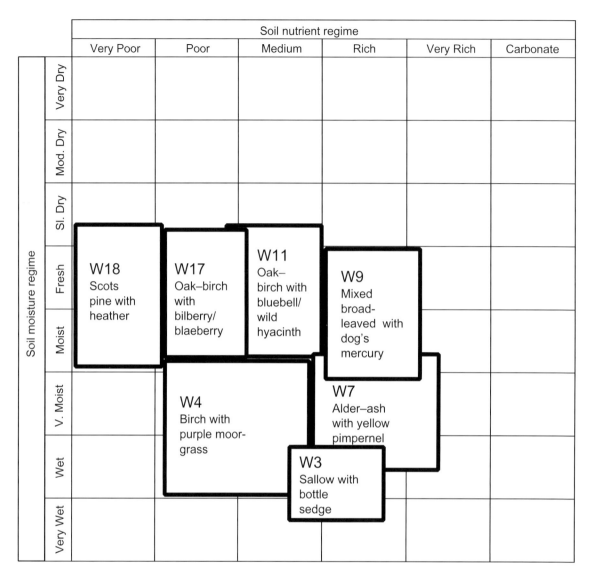

Figure 21 Very suitable soil quality for native woodlands in Warm wet, Cool moist and Cool wet climatic zones (the 'Upland Zone' of FC Bulletin 112).

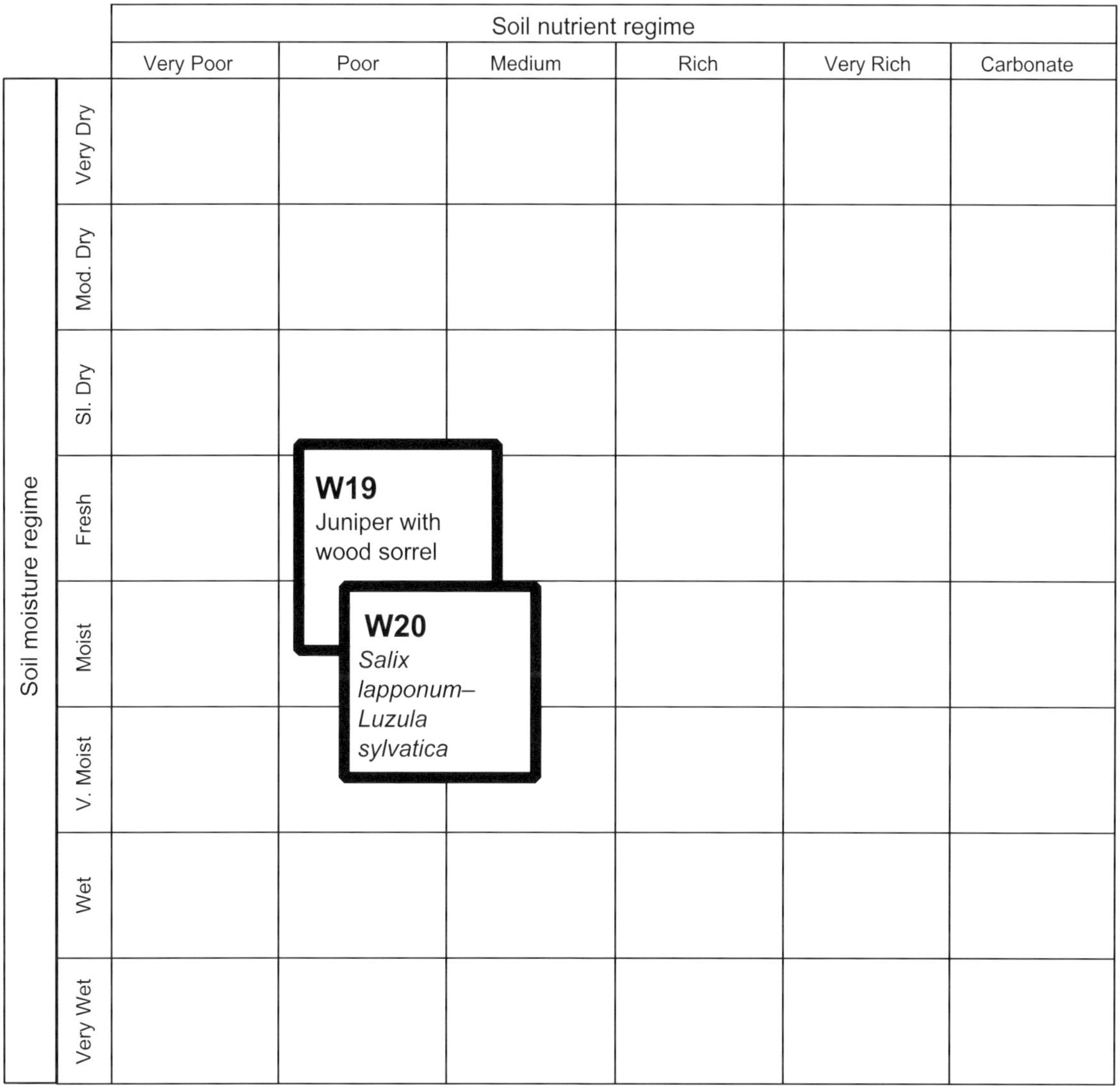

Figure 22 Very suitable soil quality for native scrub woodlands in the Sub-alpine zone (the 'Upland juniper zone' of FC Bulletin 112).

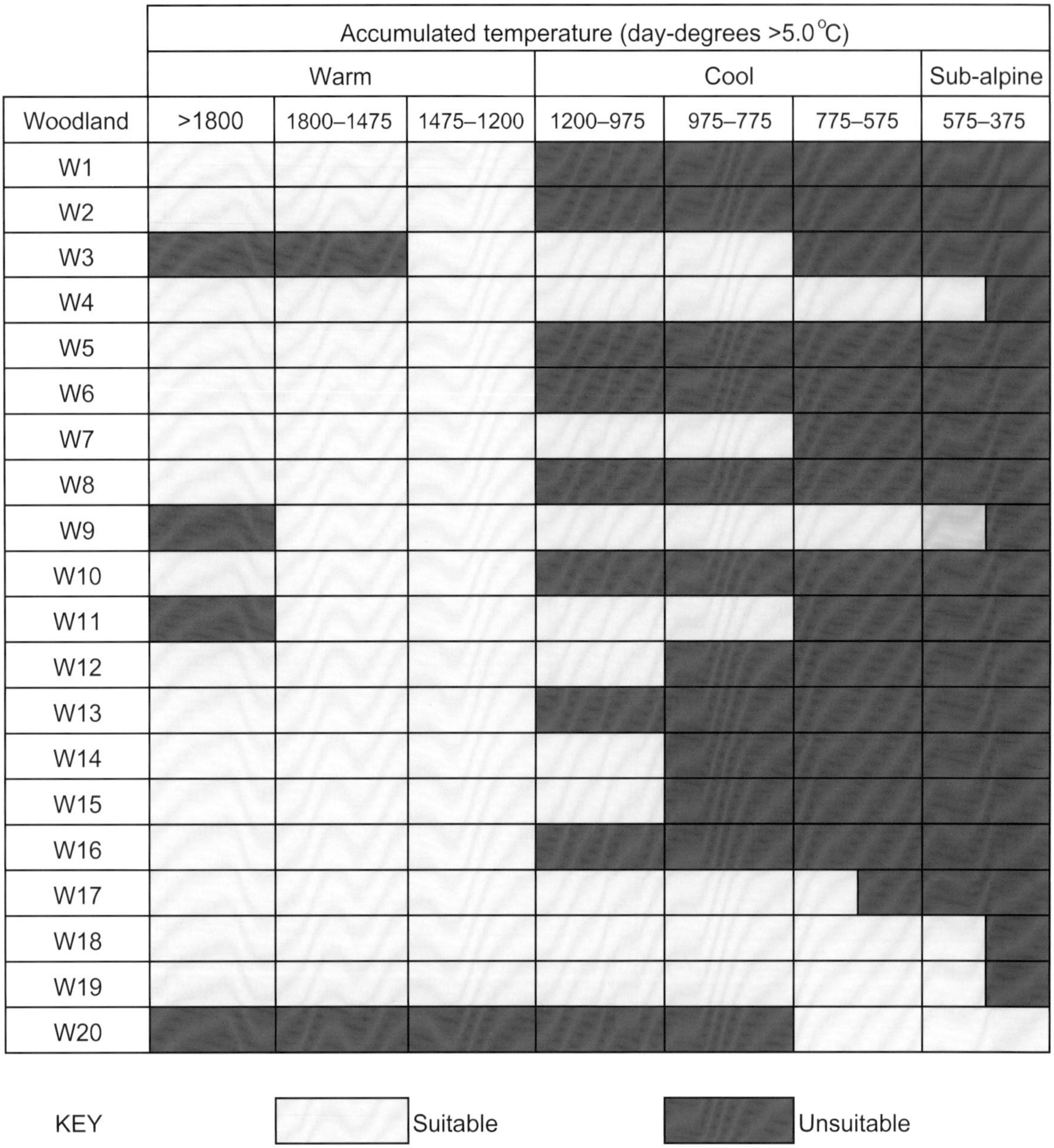

	Accumulated temperature (day-degrees >5.0°C)						
	Warm			Cool			Sub-alpine
Woodland	>1800	1800–1475	1475–1200	1200–975	975–775	775–575	575–375
W1	Suitable	Suitable	Suitable	Unsuitable	Unsuitable	Unsuitable	Unsuitable
W2	Suitable	Suitable	Suitable	Unsuitable	Unsuitable	Unsuitable	Unsuitable
W3	Unsuitable	Unsuitable	Suitable	Suitable	Suitable	Unsuitable	Unsuitable
W4	Suitable	Suitable	Suitable	Suitable	Suitable	Suitable	Suitable
W5	Suitable	Suitable	Suitable	Unsuitable	Unsuitable	Unsuitable	Unsuitable
W6	Suitable	Suitable	Suitable	Unsuitable	Unsuitable	Unsuitable	Unsuitable
W7	Suitable	Suitable	Suitable	Suitable	Unsuitable	Unsuitable	Unsuitable
W8	Suitable	Suitable	Suitable	Unsuitable	Unsuitable	Unsuitable	Unsuitable
W9	Unsuitable	Suitable	Suitable	Suitable	Suitable	Suitable	Suitable
W10	Suitable	Suitable	Suitable	Unsuitable	Unsuitable	Unsuitable	Unsuitable
W11	Unsuitable	Suitable	Suitable	Suitable	Suitable	Unsuitable	Unsuitable
W12	Suitable	Suitable	Suitable	Suitable	Unsuitable	Unsuitable	Unsuitable
W13	Suitable	Suitable	Suitable	Unsuitable	Unsuitable	Unsuitable	Unsuitable
W14	Suitable	Suitable	Suitable	Suitable	Unsuitable	Unsuitable	Unsuitable
W15	Suitable	Suitable	Suitable	Suitable	Suitable	Unsuitable	Unsuitable
W16	Suitable	Suitable	Suitable	Unsuitable	Unsuitable	Unsuitable	Unsuitable
W17	Suitable	Suitable	Suitable	Suitable	Suitable	Suitable	Unsuitable
W18	Suitable	Suitable	Suitable	Suitable	Suitable	Suitable	Suitable
W19	Suitable	Suitable	Suitable	Suitable	Suitable	Suitable	Suitable
W20	Unsuitable	Unsuitable	Unsuitable	Unsuitable	Unsuitable	Suitable	Suitable

KEY — Suitable / Unsuitable

Figure 23 Suitability of native woodlands W1–W20 by accumulated temperature.

| Woodland | Moisture deficit (mm) | | | | | | | | |
| | Wet | | | Moist | | | Dry | | |
	<20	20–60	60–90	90–120	120–140	140–160	160–180	180–200	>200
W1	Unsuitable	Unsuitable	Unsuitable						
W2	Unsuitable	Unsuitable	Unsuitable						
W3	Unsuitable	Unsuitable						Unsuitable	Unsuitable
W4									
W5	Unsuitable	Unsuitable	Unsuitable						
W6									
W7									
W8	Unsuitable	Unsuitable	Unsuitable						
W9	Unsuitable	Unsuitable	Unsuitable				Unsuitable	Unsuitable	Unsuitable
W10									
W11									Unsuitable
W12	Unsuitable	Unsuitable	Unsuitable						
W13	Unsuitable	Unsuitable	Unsuitable	Unsuitable					
W14	Unsuitable	Unsuitable	Unsuitable						
W15	Unsuitable	Unsuitable	Unsuitable						
W16	Unsuitable	Unsuitable	Unsuitable						
W17							Unsuitable	Unsuitable	Unsuitable
W18									
W19									
W20					Unsuitable	Unsuitable	Unsuitable	Unsuitable	Unsuitable

KEY   ☐ Suitable   ▨ Unsuitable

Figure 24 Suitability of native woodlands W1–W20 by moisture deficit.

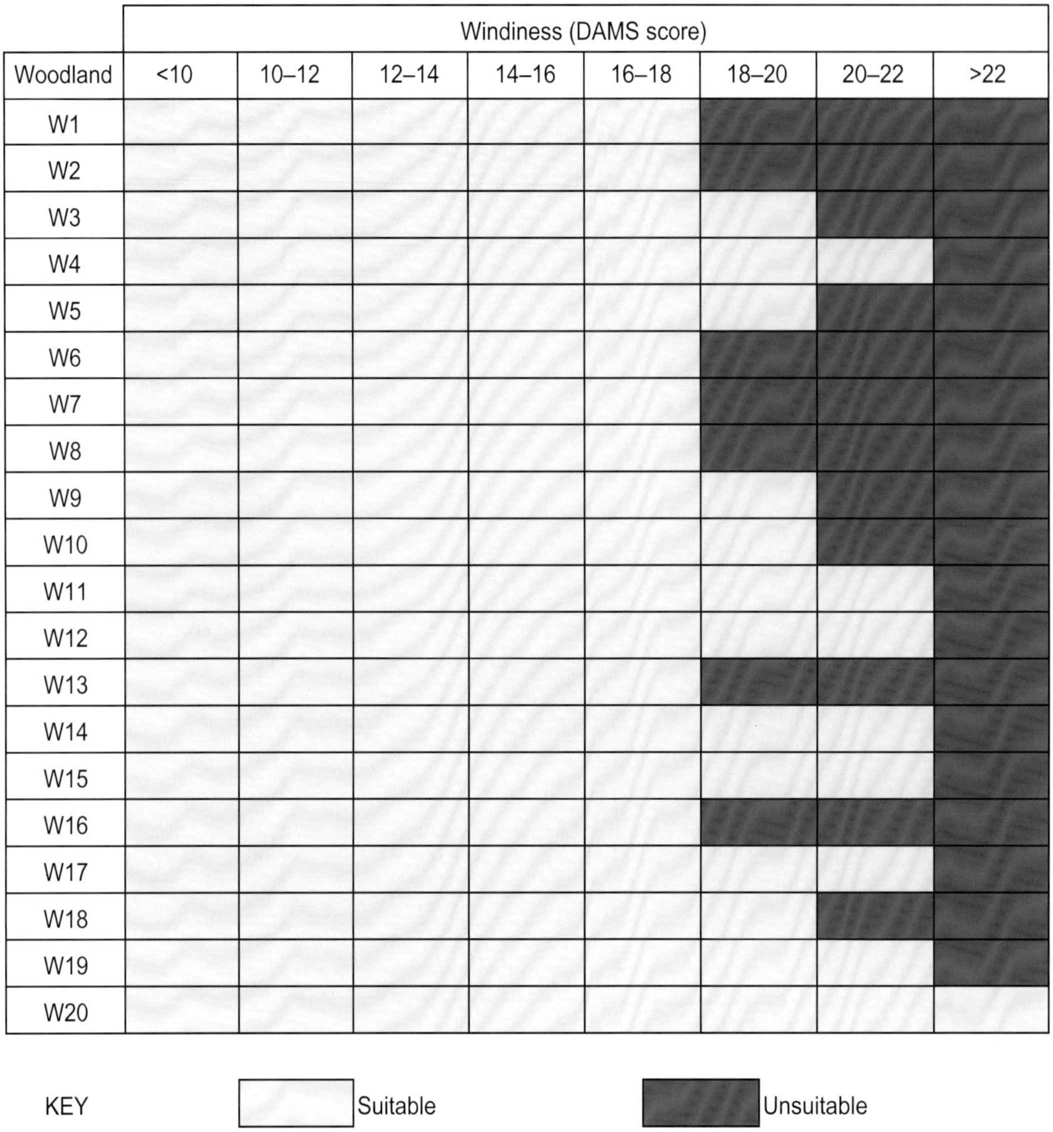

Woodland	Windiness (DAMS score)							
	<10	10–12	12–14	14–16	16–18	18–20	20–22	>22
W1	Suitable	Suitable	Suitable	Suitable	Suitable	Unsuitable	Unsuitable	Unsuitable
W2	Suitable	Suitable	Suitable	Suitable	Suitable	Unsuitable	Unsuitable	Unsuitable
W3	Suitable	Suitable	Suitable	Suitable	Suitable	Suitable	Unsuitable	Unsuitable
W4	Suitable	Suitable	Suitable	Suitable	Suitable	Suitable	Suitable	Unsuitable
W5	Suitable	Suitable	Suitable	Suitable	Suitable	Suitable	Unsuitable	Unsuitable
W6	Suitable	Suitable	Suitable	Suitable	Suitable	Unsuitable	Unsuitable	Unsuitable
W7	Suitable	Suitable	Suitable	Suitable	Suitable	Unsuitable	Unsuitable	Unsuitable
W8	Suitable	Suitable	Suitable	Suitable	Suitable	Unsuitable	Unsuitable	Unsuitable
W9	Suitable	Suitable	Suitable	Suitable	Suitable	Suitable	Unsuitable	Unsuitable
W10	Suitable	Suitable	Suitable	Suitable	Suitable	Unsuitable	Unsuitable	Unsuitable
W11	Suitable	Suitable	Suitable	Suitable	Suitable	Suitable	Suitable	Unsuitable
W12	Suitable	Suitable	Suitable	Suitable	Suitable	Suitable	Suitable	Unsuitable
W13	Suitable	Suitable	Suitable	Suitable	Suitable	Unsuitable	Unsuitable	Unsuitable
W14	Suitable	Suitable	Suitable	Suitable	Suitable	Suitable	Suitable	Unsuitable
W15	Suitable	Suitable	Suitable	Suitable	Suitable	Suitable	Suitable	Unsuitable
W16	Suitable	Suitable	Suitable	Suitable	Suitable	Unsuitable	Unsuitable	Unsuitable
W17	Suitable	Suitable	Suitable	Suitable	Suitable	Suitable	Suitable	Unsuitable
W18	Suitable	Suitable	Suitable	Suitable	Suitable	Suitable	Unsuitable	Unsuitable
W19	Suitable	Suitable	Suitable	Suitable	Suitable	Suitable	Suitable	Unsuitable
W20	Suitable	Suitable	Suitable	Suitable	Suitable	Suitable	Suitable	Suitable

KEY   ☐ Suitable   ■ Unsuitable

Figure 25 Suitability of native woodlands W1–W20 by windiness.

Woodland	Continentality			
	<5	5–7	7–9	>9
W1				
W2				
W3				
W4				
W5				
W6				
W7				
W8				
W9				▓
W10				
W11	**a,b**	**a,b**,c,d	**a,b**,c,d	▓
W12				
W13				
W14				
W15				
W16	**b**	**b**	**b**,a	a,b
W17	**a,b,c**	**a,b,c**,d	**a,b,c**,d	▓
W18	e	**a,b,c,d**	**a,b,c,d**	**a,b,c,d**
W19				
W20				

☐ Suitable, or suitable for more important sub-communities (as listed)

▓ Unsuitable

Most important sub-communities within each community are shown in **bold** type

Figure 26 Suitability of native woodlands W1–W20 by continentality.

Woodland	Very Wet	Wet	Very Moist	Moist	Fresh	Slightly Dry	Moderately Dry	Very Dry
				Soil moisture regime				
W1								
W2	**a**,b	**a**,b						
W3								
W4	c,**b**	c,**b**	b,a	a				
W5	a,**b**,c	a,**b**,c	c					
W6		a,b	a,b,**d**,e	**d,e**				
W7		**b**	a,b	c				
W8					a-d,**e-g**	a-d,**e-g**	a-d,**e-g**	
W9			a,b	a,b	a,b			
W10				**a,b,c,d,e**	**a,b,c,d,e**	**a,b,c,d,e**	**a,b,c,d,e**	
W11				a,**b,c**,d	a,**b,c**,d	a,**b,c**,d		
W12					a,b	**a,b**,c	**a,b**,c	
W13					a,**b**	a,**b**	a,**b**	
W14								
W15					**a,b,c**,d	**a,b,c**,d	**a,b,c**,d	
W16					a,**b**	a,**b**	a,**b**	
W17				a,d	**b,c**	**b,c**		
W18			d	d,e	**b,c**,e	a		
W19				a,b	a,b			
W20								

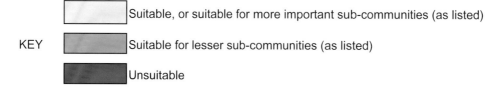

KEY

☐ Suitable, or suitable for more important sub-communities (as listed)

▨ Suitable for lesser sub-communities (as listed)

▓ Unsuitable

Most important sub-communities within each community are shown in **bold** type

Figure 27 Suitability of native woodlands W1–W20 by soil moisture regime.

Woodland	Soil nutrient regime					
	Very Poor	Poor	Medium	Rich	Very Rich	Carbonate
W1						
W2			b	a,b	a	
W3						
W4		c,**b**	**b**,a			
W5				a,**b**,c	a,**b**,c	
W6				e	a,b,**d**,e	
W7			b,c	b,c	a	
W8					**a**-d,**e**-g	
W9				b	**a**,b	
W10			d	**a**,b,c,d,**e**		
W11		**c**	a,**b**,**c**,d	a		
W12					**a**,b,c	b,c
W13					a,**b**	a
W14						
W15		c,d	**a**,**b**			
W16		a,**b**	a,**b**			
W17		a,**b**,d	c			
W18	a,**b**,d,e	**c**				
W19		a	b			
W20						

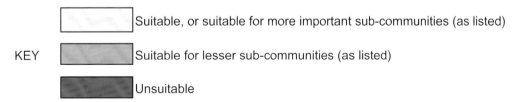

KEY

☐ Suitable, or suitable for more important sub-communities (as listed)

▨ Suitable for lesser sub-communities (as listed)

▮ Unsuitable

Most important sub-communities within each community are shown in **bold** type

Figure 28 Suitability of native woodlands W1–W20 by soil nutrient regime.

References

Adamson, J. K., Hornung, M., Pyatt, D. G. and Anderson, A. R. (1987). Changes in solute chemistry of drainage waters following the clearfelling of a Sitka spruce plantation. *Forestry* **60** (2), 165–177.

Aldhous, J. R. and Low, A. J. (1974). *The potential of western hemlock, western red cedar, grand fir and noble fir in Britain.* Forestry Commission Bulletin 49. HMSO, London.

Anderson, M. L. (1950). *The selection of tree species.* Oliver & Boyd, Edinburgh.

Anderson, M. L. and Fairbairn, W. A. (1955). *Division of Scotland into climatic sub-regions as an aid to silviculture.* Bulletin of the Forestry Department No. 1. University of Edinburgh, Scotland.

Anon. (1991a). *Le fichier écologique des essences, 1: texte explicatif.* Ministère de la Région Wallonne, Namur, Belgium.

Anon. (1991b). *Le fichier écologique des essences, 2: le fichier écologique.* Ministère de la Région Wallonne, Namur, Belgium.

Barrow, E., Hulme, M. and Jiang, T. (1993). *A 1961–90 baseline climatology and future climate change scenarios for Great Britain and Europe. Part I: 1961–90 Great Britain baseline climatology.* Climate Research Unit, University of East Anglia, Norwich. 50 pp.

Bendelow, V. C. and Hartnup, R. (1980). *Climatic classification of England and Wales.* Soil Survey Technical Monograph No. 15. Rothamsted Experimental Station, Harpenden. 27 pp.

Binns, W. O., Mayhead, G. J. and MacKenzie, J. M. (1980). *Nutrient deficiencies of conifers in British forests.* Forestry Commission Leaflet 76. HMSO, London.

Birse, E. L. (1971). *Assessment of climatic conditions in Scotland, 3: The bioclimatic sub-regions.* Macaulay Land Use Research Institute, Aberdeen. 12 pp.

Birse, E. L. and Dry, F. T. (1970). *Assessment of climatic conditions in Scotland, 1: Based on accumulated temperature and potential water deficit.* Macaulay Land Use Research Institute, Aberdeen. 25 pp.

Birse, E. L. and Robertson, L. (1970). *Assessment of climatic conditions in Scotland, 2: Based on exposure and accumulated frost.* Macaulay Land Use Research Institute, Aberdeen. 41 pp.

Blamey, M. and Grey-Wilson, C. (1989). *The illustrated flora of Great Britain and northern Europe.* Hodder & Stoughton, London.

Brethes, A., Brun, J-J., Jabiol, B., Ponge, J. and Toutain, F. (1995). Classification of forest humus forms: a French proposal. *Annales des Sciences Forestières* **52** (6), 535–546.

Cajander, A. K. (1926). The theory of forest types. *Acta Forestalia Fennica* **29** (3), 1–108.

Day, W. R. (1957). *Sitka spruce in British Columbia: a study in forest relationships.*, Forestry Commission Bulletin 28. HMSO, London.

Edwards, P. N. and Christie, J. M. (1981). *Yield models for forest management.* Forestry Commission Booklet 48. Forestry Commission, Edinburgh.

Ellenberg, H. (1988). *Vegetation ecology of Central Europe,* 4th edtn (English). Cambridge University Press, Cambridge.

Ellenberg, H., Weber, H. E., Dull, R., Wirth, V., Werner, W. and Paulissen, D. (1992). *Zeigerwerte von pflanzen in Mitteleuropa.* Scripta Geobotanica Vol. 18, 2nd edtn. Goltze, Gottingen. 258 pp.

Evans, J. (1984). *Silviculture of broadleaved woodland.* Forestry Commission Bulletin 62. HMSO, London.

Fairbairn, W. A. (1960). Climatic zonation in England and Wales. *International Journal of Bioclimatology and Biometeorology* **IV** (II), section C. 20 pp.

Field Studies Council (1988). *Key to common grasses.* Field Studies Council, Preston Montford, Montford Bridge, Shrewsbury, SY4 1HW.

Field Studies Council (1998a). *A key to plants common in woodland.* Field Studies Council, Preston Montford, Montford Bridge, Shrewsbury, SY4 1HW.

Field Studies Council (1998b). *A key to plants common on moorlands.* Field Studies Council, Preston Montford, Montford Bridge, Shrewsbury, SY4 1HW.

Forestry Commission (1998). *The UK forestry standard.* Forestry Commission, Edinburgh.

Forestry Commission (2001). *Ecological site classification: a PC-based decision support system for British forests.* Forestry Commission, Edinburgh. (Manual + CD-ROM.)

Franklin, J. F. and Dyrness, C. T. (1973). *Natural vegetation of Oregon and Washington.* USDA Forest Service General Technical Report PNW–8. USDA Forest Service, Portland, Oregon.

Garrard, I. and Streeter, D. (1998). *The wild flowers of the British Isles.* Midsummer Books, London.

Gilchrist, W. (1872). On the soils best suited for the different kinds of forest trees, as indicated by the plants that grow naturally upon them. *Transactions of the Royal Arboricultural Society* **VI,** 296–303.

Green, R. N., Trowbridge, R. L. and Klinka, K. (1993). *Towards a taxonomic classification of humus forms.* Forest Science Monograph 29. Society of American Foresters, Bethesda, MD. 49 pp.

Hall, D. G. M., Reeve, M. G., Thomasson, A. J. and Wright, V. F. (1977). *Water retention, porosity and density of field soils.* Soil Survey Technical Monograph No. 9. Rothamsted Experimental Station, Harpenden.

Hall, J. (1998). *An analysis of National Vegetation Classification survey data.* Report No. 272. Joint Nature Conservation Committee, Northminster House, Peterborough.

Harmer, R. and Kerr, G. (1995). *Natural regeneration of broadleaved trees.* Forestry Commission Research Information Note 275. Forestry Commission, Edinburgh.

Hill, M. O., Mountford, J. O., Roy, D. B. and Bunce, R. G. H. (1999). *Ellenberg's indicator values for British plants.* ECOFACT Volume 2, Technical Annex. Institute of Terrestrial Ecology, Huntingdon.

Hodgson, J. M. (1974). *Soil Survey field handbook.* Technical Monograph No. 5. Soil Survey of England and Wales, Harpenden. (3rd edtn., 1997).

Jabiol, B., Brethes, A., Ponge, J-F., Toutain, F. and Brun, J-J. (1995). *L'humus sous toutes ses formes.* École Nationale du Génie Rural, des Eaux et des Forêts, Nancy. 63 pp.

Katzensteiner, K., Englisch, M. and Hager, H. (in preparation.). Taxonomy of forest humus forms, a proposal for a European classification.

Kennedy, F. M. (2001). *The identification of soils for forestry.* Forestry Commission Field Book 19. Forestry Commission, Edinburgh.

Klinka, K., Krajina, V. J., Ceska, A. and Scagel, A. M. (1989). *Indicator plants of coastal British Columbia.* UBC Press, Vancouver, BC. 288 pp.

Krajina, V. J. (1969). Ecology of forest trees in British Columbia. In, *Ecology of western North America*, Vol. **2,** 1–146, ed. V. J. Krajina. University of British Columbia, Department of Botany.

Landon, J. R. (1988). Toward a standard field assessment of soil texture for mineral soils. *Soil Survey and Land Evaluation* **8**, 161–165.

Lines, R. (1987). *Choice of seed origins for the main forest species in Britain.* Forestry Commission Bulletin 66. HMSO, London.

Macdonald, J. (1952). The place of north-western American conifers in British Forestry. *Sixth British Commonwealth Forestry Conference*, Canada, Item 7a Silviculture. 21 pp.

Macdonald, J., Wood, R. F., Edwards, M. V. and Aldhous, J. R. (1957). *Exotic forest trees in Great Britain.* Forestry Commission Bulletin 30. HMSO, London.

Nixon, C. J. and Worrell, R. (1999). *The potential for the natural regeneration of conifers in Britain.* Forestry Commission Bulletin 120. Forestry Commission, Edinburgh.

Ontario Institute of Pedology (1985). *Field manual for describing soils.* 3rd edition. Ontario Institute of Pedology and University of Guelph, Ontario. OIP Publication 85–3.

Peterken, G. F. (1981). *Woodland conservation and management.* Chapman and Hall, London. (2nd edition, 1993).

Phillips, R. (1980). *Grasses, ferns, mosses and lichens of Great Britain and Ireland.* Pan Books, London.

Pojar, J., Klinka, K. and Meidinger, D. (1987). Biogeoclimatic ecosystem classification in British Columbia. *Forest Ecology and Management* **22**, 119–154.

Pyatt, D. G. (1970). *Soil groups of upland forests.* Forestry Commission Forest Record 71. HMSO, London.

Pyatt, D. G. (1977). *Guide to site types in forests of north and mid Wales.* Forestry Commission Forest Record 69. HMSO, London.

Pyatt, D. G. (1982). *Soil classification.* Forestry Commission Research Information Note 68/82/SSN. Forestry Commission, Edinburgh.

Pyatt, D. G. (1997). A site classification for Scottish native woodlands. *Botanical Journal of Scotland* **49** (2), 455–467.

Pyatt, D. G. and Smith, K. A. (1983). Water and oxygen regimes of four soil types at Newcastleton Forest, south Scotland. *Journal of Soil Science* **34**, 465–482.

Pyatt, D. G., Spencer, J. W., Hutchby, L., Davani, S., Fletcher, J. and Purdy, K. (2001). *Applying the ecological site classification in the lowlands – a case study of the New Forest inclosures.* Forestry Commission Technical Paper 33. Forestry Commission, Edinburgh.

Pyatt, D. G. and Suárez, J. C. (1997). *An ecological site classification for forestry in Great Britain with special reference to Grampian, Scotland.* Forestry Commission Technical Paper 20. Forestry Commission, Edinburgh.

Quine, C. P. (2000). Estimation of mean wind climate and probability of strong winds from assessments of relative windiness. *Forestry* **73** (3), 247–258.

Quine, C. P. and White, I. M. S. (1993). *Revised windiness scores for the windthrow hazard classification: the revised scoring method.* Forestry Commission Research Information Note 230. Forestry Commission, Edinburgh.

Quine, C. P. and White, I. M. S. (1994). Using the relationship between rate of tatter and topographic variables to predict site windiness in upland britain. *Forestry* **67** (3), 245–256.

Rameau, J. C., Mansion, D. and Dumé, G. (1989). *Flore forestière française: guide écologique illustré; Vol 1: Plaines et collines.* Institut pour le Développement Forestier, Ministère de l'Agriculture et de la Pêche, Paris. 1785 pp.

Rameau, J. C., Mansion, D. and Dumé, G. (1993). *Flore forestière française: guide écologique illustré; Vol 2: Montagnes.* Institut pour le Développement Forestier, Ministère de l'Agriculture et de la Pêche, Paris. 2421 pp.

Ray, D. and Nicoll, B. (1994). Effects of soil water on root development and stability of Sitka spruce. *Journal of Experimental Botany* **46** (supplement), 47.

Robson, J. D. and Thomasson, A. J. (1977). *Soil water regimes.* Soil Survey Technical Monograph No. 11. Rothamsted Experimental Station, Harpenden. 57 pp.

Rodwell, J. S. (ed.) (1991). *British plant communities, I: Woodlands and scrub.* Cambridge University Press, Cambridge.

Rodwell, J. S. and Patterson, G. S. (1994). *Creating new native woodlands.* Forestry Commission Bulletin 112. HMSO, London.

Rose, F. (1989). *Colour identification guide to the grasses, sedges, rushes and ferns of the British Isles and north-western Europe.* Viking – Penguin Books, London.

Savill, P. S. (1991). *The silviculture of trees used in British forestry.* C.A.B. International, Wallingford.

Schmidt, R. L. (1957). *The silvics and plant geography of the genus Abies.* Technical Publication T 46. Department of Lands and Forests, British Columbia Forest Service.

Stace, C. (1997). *New flora of the British Isles* (2nd edition). Cambridge University Press, Cambridge.

Taylor, C. M. A. (1991). *Forest fertilisation in Britain.* Forestry Commission Bulletin 95. HMSO, London.

Taylor, C. M. A. and Tabbush, P. M. (1990). *Nitrogen deficiency in Sitka spruce plantations.* Forestry Commission Bulletin 89. HMSO, London.

Thompson, N., Barrie, I. A. and Ayles, M. (1981). *The Meteorological Office rainfall and evaporation calculation system: MORECS (July 1981).* Meteorological Office Hydrological Memorandum N45.

Weissen, F., Bronchart, L. and Piret, A. (1994). *Guide de boisement des stations forestières de Wallonie.* Direction Generale des Ressources Naturelles et de l'Environnement, Jambes, Belgium.

Whitbread, A. M. and Kirby, K. J. (1992). *Summary of National Vegetation Classification woodland descriptions.* UK Nature Conservation No. 4. Joint Nature Conservation Committee, Peterborough.

White, G. S. A., Pyatt, D. G., Quine, C. P., Fletcher, J., Clare, J., Connolly, T. and Worrell, R. (2000). *New climate data for ecological site classification in British forestry.* Unpublished paper. Forest Research, Roslin Midlothian.

Wilson, S.M. (1998). *The quantification of soil nutrient regime in British forests and its assessment from ground vegetation and humus type.* Unpublished PhD thesis, University of Edinburgh.

Wilson, S. M., Pyatt, D. G., Malcolm, D. C. and Connolly, T. (1998). Ecological site classification: soil nutrient regime in British woodlands. *Scottish Forestry* **52** (2), 86–92.

Wood, R. F. (1955). *Studies of north-west American forests in relation to silviculture in Great Britain.* Forestry Commission Bulletin 25. HMSO, London.

Wood, R. F. and Nimmo, M. (1962). *Chalk downland afforestation.* Forestry Commission Bulletin 34. HMSO, London.

Appendix 1

The assessment of soil texture and available water capacity

As mentioned in Chapter 3, the assessment of soil texture is a part of the estimate of the available water capacity of soil. The ESC method only requires recognition of organic, sandy, coarse loamy, fine loamy and clayey textures. Two methods for the assessment of soil texture are given as Figures 29 and 30. The methods are more detailed than is actually necessary. Both methods should give the same results most of the time, but individual users tend to prefer one method over the other. After one method has been used on a soil sample, it is a good idea to check the result using the other method. Figure 31 shows how the more detailed classes of texture given in Figures 29 and 30 are related to the broader ESC classes of texture.

The available water capacity of the soil is estimated using the method in Figure 32. Although the method is as simple as possible, it allows for the possible existence of two different layers within the soil. The method does not cater for soils with a water-table within the rooting zone. Such soils are considered to fall into the Moist to Very Wet classes of moisture regime and do not need an estimate of available water capacity.

Start with a 2.5 cm diameter mass of soil at the sticky point. Sticky point is defined as the moisture content at which dry soil being gradually moistened just begins to adhere to the fingers.

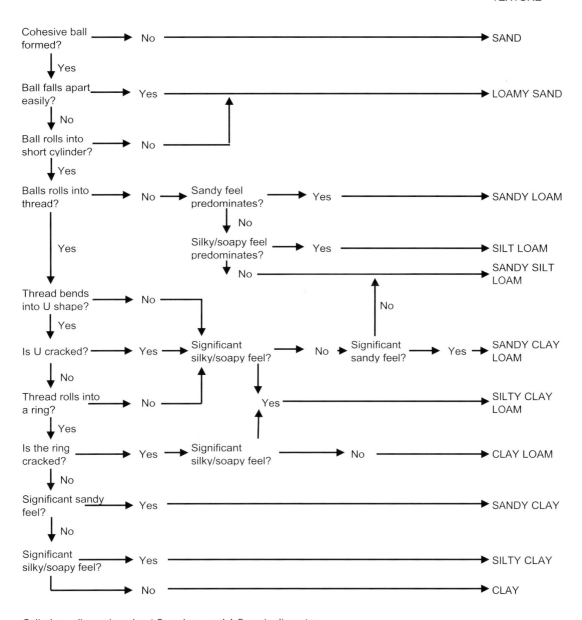

Cylinder = dimension about 5 cm long and 1.5 cm in diameter.
Thread = about 13 cm long and 0.6 cm in diameter.
Ring = a circle about 2.5 cm in diameter formed from an 8 cm section of thread.

Figure 29 Assessment of soil texture, method 1 (after Landon, 1988).

Start with a 2.5 cm diameter mass of soil at the sticky point. Sticky point is defined as the moisture content at which dry soil being gradually moistened just begins to adhere to the fingers.

Sandy-ness	Smoothness	Stickiness and plasticity	Ball and thread formation	Texture
Extremely sandy	Not smooth	Not sticky or plastic	Non cohesive balls which collapse easily.	Sand
		Not sticky or plastic	Slightly cohesive balls, does not form threads.	Loamy sand
Very sandy	Not smooth	Not sticky or plastic	Slightly cohesive balls, does not form threads.	Sandy loam
Moderately sandy	Slightly smooth	Slightly sticky and plastic	Moderately cohesive balls, forms threads with great difficulty.	Sandy silt loam
	Not smooth	Moderately sticky and plastic	Moderately cohesive balls, forms long threads which bend into rings with difficulty. Moderate degree of polish.	Sandy clay loam
	Not smooth	Very sticky and plastic	Very cohesive balls, forms long threads which bend into rings with difficulty. High degree of polish.	Sandy clay
Slightly to moderately sandy	Slightly smooth	Moderately sticky and plastic	Very cohesive balls, forms threads which will bend into rings.	Clay loam
Non-sandy to slightly sandy	Very smooth and silky	Slightly sticky and plastic	Moderately cohesive balls, forms threads with great difficulty that have broken appearance. No polish.	Silt loam
	Moderately smooth and silky	Moderately sticky and plastic	Moderately cohesive balls, forms threads which will not bend into rings. Moderate degree of polish.	Silty clay loam
		Very sticky and plastic	Very cohesive balls and long threads which bend into rings. High degree of polish.	Silty clay
	Not smooth	Extremely sticky and plastic	Extremely cohesive balls and long threads which bend into rings easily. High degree of polish.	Clay

Cylinder = dimension about 5 cm long and 1.5 cm in diameter.
Thread = about 13 cm long and 0.6 cm in diameter.
Ring = a circle about 2.5 cm in diameter formed from an 8 cm section of thread.

Figure 30 Assessment of soil texture, method 2.

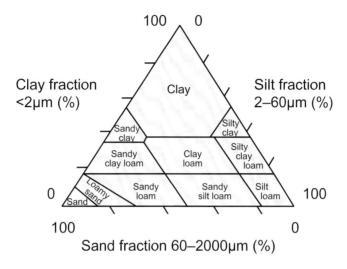

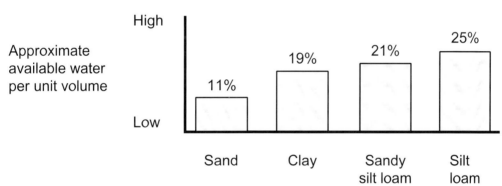

Figure 31 Soil texture classes (after Hodgson, 1997).

Layered soils: For a soil with two very different layers, e.g. a layer of peat over mineral, separate calculations should be made for each layer and summed. (In many cases the two layers will conveniently form the main and secondary rooting zones.)

Step 1: Soil texture of main rooting zone   AWC/m

Start here │ Soil extremely stony, with sandy matrix │————— yes ————— 50mm

no

│ Soil sand or loamy sand │————— yes ————— 100mm

no

│ Soil loamy or clayey │————— yes ————— 170mm

no

│ Humus layer or soil peaty │————— yes ————— 400mm

Step 2: Depth of main rooting zone

Multiply the AWC/m by the depth of the main rooting zone in metres, e.g. if the depth is 70 cm multiply by 0.7.
(The main rooting zone is that part of the soil that is likely to be uplifted with the root system if the tree is windthrown.)

Step 3: Stoniness of main rooting zone

Soils that are extremely stony (AWC 50 mm/m depth) need no further adjustment. For other soils reduce the AWC obtained so far by the volumetric proportion of stones. For example, if there are 15% stones, multiply value by 0.85.
(It is easy to over-estimate the volumetric proportion of stones. Even the extremely stony fluvioglacial gravels with most stones in contact with each other have a maximum of 60% stones by volume, provided the matrix fills the interstices.)

Step 4: Secondary rooting zone

Repeat steps 1–3, for the secondary rooting zone, but finally multiply its contribution to AWC by 0.5.
(The secondary rooting zone may have very few roots (e.g. < 1/dm^2) but can be a major source of moisture during droughts. If in doubt about depth, err on the generous side.)

Step 5: Add the contributions from the main and secondary rooting zones.

Figure 32 Estimating the available water capacity (AWC) of the soil.

Appendix 2

Classification of humus forms

The classification of humus forms for assessing soil nutrient regime is dealt with in Chapter 5. The classification used (Figure 33) is a simplified version of that proposed by Katzensteiner *et al.* (in preparation). The various forms of peat are excluded because their soil quality is adequately dealt with by the classification of forest soil types (Appendix 4) or by the use of indicator plants.

1a. Either L only or L+F horizons present; H if present is very thin or discontinuous. A horizon (> 2 cm thick) with organic and mineral material blended together in aggregates (crumbs or blocks), earthworms present. Sharp break between organic and A horizon.	Mull

1b. L, F and H horizons present and continuous.

2a. Gradual transition between H and A horizon. A horizon with few or no earthworms, organic and mineral particles usually separate (use hand lens), but may be blended. Many faecal pellets.	Moder
2b. Sharp break between the H horizon and an A horizon which is sometimes black and humic, but often light coloured. Usually fungal mycelium present. Few faecal pellets. Earthworms absent or rare.	Mor

Mulls can be further sub-divided:

3a. Ln present but Lv and F absent. Breakdown of litter very rapid. Many earthworms.	Eumull

3b. Ln + Lv + F present. Breakdown of litter fairly slow. Fewer earthworms.

4a. F horizon may be discontinuous, H absent.	Oligomull
4b. F horizon continuous, H discontinuous or very thin.	Moder-like mull

Definition of humus horizons

L   Fairly fresh plant residues, readily identifiable as to origin. No fine decomposed material.

Ln (n = new): Fresh litter that has not undergone decomposition; the leaves remain whole, only their colour may have changed. In soils with very rapid breakdown of litter, this horizon only exists from autumn to the beginning of spring.

Lv: Litter showing little fragmentation, but changed due to colour, cohesion or hardness. If present, underlies the Ln horizon.

F   Fragmented material in which plant structures are generally recognisable as to origin, and mixed with some (<70%) finely decomposed organic matter (e.g. faecal pellets). Often contains roots and fungal mycelia. Plant remains are densely overlapping.

H   Contains >70% fine organic material (ignoring roots) in which plant structures are generally not recognisable. Reddish brown to black in colour, fairly homogeneous in appearance. Mineral grains may be present. Horizon often more coherent than the underlying horizon. [This horizon is distinguished from peat (O horizon) by being formed in conditions that are not saturated with water for more than 6 months in the year.]

A   Horizons containing a mixture of organic and mineral material (< 30% organic matter).

Figure 33 Key to the humus forms of Figure 8.

(simplified European system, after Katzensteiner *et al.*, in preparation)

Appendix 3

Description of soil profile

Introduction: recording information relevant to soil moisture and nutrient regimes

In order to assess soil moisture and nutrient regimes, the user of ESC may need to make a simple soil description including soil type, lithology, humus form, rooting depth and available water capacity. In addition, a description of the ground vegetation around the soil pit (method described in Chapter 6) will help provide a refinement of the assessment of soil nutrient regime.

If the soil profile has more than one distinct layer or *horizon*, each should be identified (see below) and described separately. The properties that should be recorded for each horizon are: colour and mottling, stoniness, texture, structure, consistence, roots and parent material of the whole profile.

The method of describing a soil profile given here is a simplified version of that provided by Hodgson (1974). Suitable forms for recording description of the site, soil profile and vegetation are given as Figures 34 and 35.

Choice of location

Avoid man-made or other obvious irregularities of the ground surface, especially where the humus layer has been disturbed or lost. Normally avoid the zone within, say, 15 m of a forest road where the soil may be affected by road dust (more important nutritionally than physically). Choose an area of uniform ground vegetation representative of the site.

Thickness of horizons

Record the thickness in cm of each layer, including the variation if this large in comparison with the average thickness of the layer. The sum of the thickness of the horizons should equal the total depth described.

Colour

Colour is one of the most important soil properties, but is open to a good deal of subjectivity. Describe the main colour and any relevant subsidiary colours, e.g. mottling, streaking or patchy coloration due to gleying. If ped surfaces (see 'Structure' below) are greyer than their interiors this may reflect gleying. (See also comments on root channels.) It is not necessary to use the pedologist's *Munsell soil colour book* but choice of colours should be limited to: brown, red, yellow and grey, with ochreous or rusty being useful for describing mottles. Colour indicates most of the soil processes. Red colours are mostly inherited from the parent material. Brown colours normally indicate good aeration, grey colours and mottled or streaked grey/yellow colours indicate gleying caused by poor aeration. Paler E horizons overlying darker or stronger colours in B horizons indicate podzolisation or clay translocation.

Stoniness

Stoniness refers to the proportion of stones. Stoniness affects water capacity. Describe stoniness using the following terms:

stone-free:	0% of soil volume
slightly stony:	<5% of soil volume
moderately stony:	5–15 of soil volume
very stony:	15–30% of soil volume
extremely stony:	>30% of soil volume.

The cover percentage charts (Figure 36) may be a help in visualising these percentages.

Texture

Texture refers to the proportion of sand (2–0.06 mm), silt (0.06–0.002 mm) and clay (<0.002 mm) sized particles. Texture influences many other properties including available water capacity, structure, aeration and nutrient retention. The assessment of texture is dealt with in Appendix 1. It is sufficient to be able to recognise the following classes: organic, sandy, coarse loamy, fine loamy, clayey, but for the four mineral classes it is also worth noting whether the material is 'humose' or 'very humose'. This can usually be assessed from the colour relative to the less humose horizon beneath and from the feel.

Structure

Structure describes the degree to which the individual sand, silt and clay particles are aggregated into natural units called 'peds'. The soil will usually need to be handled before this structure is fully evident. If the topsoil is well worked by earthworms it will be strongly aggregated into small blocky or crumb-like peds reminiscent of the well-raked tilth of a garden soil. Other soils, including subsoils, may be strongly aggregated due to high content of iron or aluminium oxides. Loamy soils are more likely to be well structured than sandy soils, which are often structureless ('single-grain'). Clayey soils are normally well structured with peds that have angular shapes, in the subsoil usually with fissures that are mainly vertical ('prismatic structure'). Indurated and some other layers have mainly horizontal fissures and are described as 'platy structured'. Soils that are cohesive but not obviously structured are described as 'massive'. A 'clod' differs from a ped in that it is made by man, usually by cultivating when the soil is too wet. It may consist of many peds or be structureless, massive. Soil structure is important in drainage and aeration, especially in loamy or clayey soils, and to root penetration. A good structure is almost invariably a 'good thing' for a loamy or clayey soil, but many sandy soils are productive regardless of their poor structure.

Structure should be described in terms of:

strength: strong, weak, absent

type: crumb, blocky, prismatic, platy,
    single-grain or massive.

Consistence

Consistence describes the hardness due to cohesion of the soil particles and has an important effect on rooting. It is influenced by texture and organic matter content but reflects other processes such as cementation. Take a clod of 2–4 cm size and press it between thumb and forefinger. Cemented or indurated material is characteristically brittle. Describe the consistence in terms of:

strength: very friable, friable, firm, very firm

type: brittle, not brittle.

Roots

The distribution of roots in a soil pit or in a windthrown root system can indicate where aeration is satisfactory and where compacted layers are present. Dead roots are usually a sign of periodic anaerobic conditions due to a fluctuating water-table. Roots can penetrate surprisingly compact or hard soil, and they can usually penetrate ironpans. They do not, however, penetrate indurated subsoils except down the occasional narrow crack. An ironpan lying directly on an indurated layer is a very effective barrier to roots. Roots make very 'determined' attempts to penetrate fissures within hard rock and the tree can gain greatly in stability from such rooting, but abraded roots are commonly found in very stony layers. Root systems exposed on the roadside are informative if they are fairly fresh, but beware the roots that have grown down the loose material on the face since being exposed. They may even re-enter the profile lower down, beneath compacted layers.

Describe the rooting in terms of:

depth (horizons)

intensity: few, many roots

size: diameter in mm or cm

condition: alive, dead, abraded.

Parent material

This refers to the material of the whole soil profile, not just the C horizon. Lithology describes the hardness, grain size and mineralogical composition of the rock from which the parent material is derived. Lithology has an important influence on soil texture, stoniness and nutrient regime. Rocks with plenty of calcium tend to produce soils with higher pH and richer soil nutrient regime. Hard lithologies tend to produce stony or shallow soils. The type of drift material from which many soils are formed will have a major influence on all soil properties. Soil materials are often layered, e.g. sandy or loamy over clayey, friable over indurated, less stony over very stony and these layers may be emphasized by soil horizons.

Describe the parent material in terms of:

map-unit number on the Geological Survey 10 miles to an inch map (British Geological Survey, 3rd edition, 1979)

geological age of parent rock

lithology including colour

layering and depth

type: glacial till, fluvio-glacial sand or gravel, scree, solifluction, alluvium, windblown sand.

Definitions of horizons

In a brief description of a soil profile for ESC purposes it is necessary only to be able to recognise the five main kinds of horizon: Organic, A, E, B and C, although for identification of humus form subdivisions of the Organic horizon are needed.

Organic   Horizon composed of organic material (>30% organic matter), usually lying on top of the mineral horizons. Is subdivided into Ln, Lv, F, H and O horizons (peat) for the purpose of identifying the humus form (Figure 33).

A   Mineral horizon (<30% organic matter) formed at or near the surface, characterised by incorporation of humified organic matter.

E   Subsurface mineral horizon that contains less organic matter and/or less iron oxide and/or less clay than the immediately underlying horizon, presumably as a result of removal of one or more of these constituents.

B   Mineral subsurface horizon characterised either by deposition (from horizons above) of clay, iron oxide, aluminium oxide or humus, or by alteration of the original material by weathering *in situ* and the formation of soil structure.

C   Relatively unaltered parent material. This may be modified by gleying due to waterlogging, accumulation of carbonates, or induration inherited from the glacial period.

The following lower case letters may be attached to the above, to indicate common types of horizon.

g   (gleyed) Colour mottled or dominantly greyish due to periodic waterlogging. The stronger colours are yellow, ochreous or rusty and represent the concentrations of iron oxide. The weaker, i.e. greyer, colours represent the loss of iron oxide. In permanently waterlogged Cg horizons the colour may be bluish or greenish due to ferrous iron compounds. Can be attached to A, E, B or C horizons.

h   (humose) Colour darkened by high concentration of humus material (but still less than 30%). Used with A or B horizons.

x   (indurated) Used to emphasise the presence of firm or very firm consistence, brittle and usually platy structure, and the characteristic silty cappings on stones. Indurated material is normally treated as a C horizon.

Note that this use of these letters is independent of their use as part of the soil type codes.

63

Horizon	Thickness	Colour and mottling	Stoniness	Texture	Structure	Consistence	Roots	Comments

Parent material	Map unit no.		Geol. age	Lithology		Layering/depth		Type	
Soil type	FC type			FC code		Series		Association	
Rooting depth		cm	Avail. water capacity		mm	Humus form		SMR	SNR

Figure 34 Ecological Site Classification: description of soil profile.

	Forest/Estate:									Grid Ref.:				
	Location:									Elevation:		m	Aspect:	
	Site description:									Distance from sea:				km
										Slope gradient:			deg. or %	
										Slope type:				
										Slope position:				
										Tree species:				
										P.Yr.:		Yield class:		
Climate: AT5:				MD:			DAMS:				Cont.			
Vegetation description:														

	Species list:	Cover in quadrat										Freq.	Max.
	tree, shrub, field and ground layers	1	2	3	4	5	6	7	8	9	10		cover
1													
2													
3													
4													
5													
6													
7													
8													
9													
10													
11													
12													
13													
14													
15													
16													
17													
18													
19													
20													
21													
22													
23													
24													
25													
Abundance weighted: SMR						SNR							

Figure 35 Ecological Site Classification: description of site and vegetation.

Each quarter of any one square has the same amount of black.

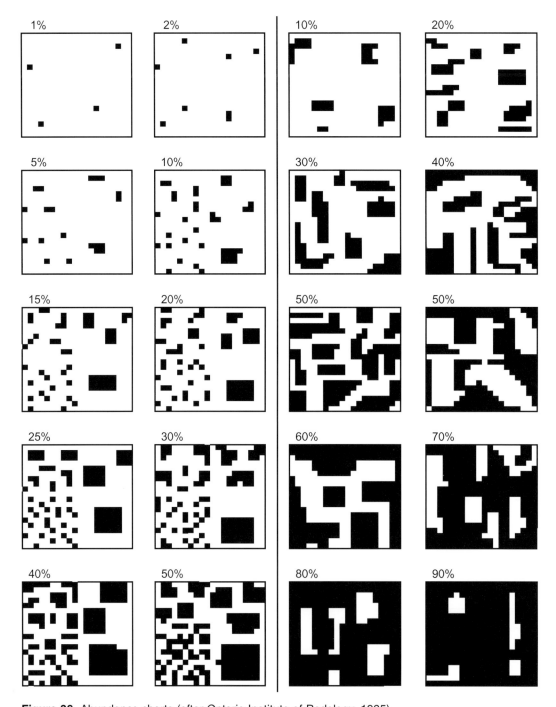

Figure 36 Abundance charts (after Ontario Institute of Pedology, 1985).

Appendix 4

Forest soil classification

Check list of soil groups, types and phases (after Pyatt, 1982).

A much fuller description of the forest soil classification is available via the 'Help files' of the ESC Decision Support System. See also Kennedy (2001).

Table 16 The main mineral and shallow peat soils (peat <45 cm)

	Soil group	Soil type	Code
Soils with well aerated subsoil	1. Brown earths	Typical brown earth	1
		Basic brown earth	1d
		Upland brown earth	1u
		Podzolic brown earth	1z
	3. Podzols	Typical podzol	3
		Hardpan podzol	3m
	4. Ironpan soils	Intergrade ironpan soil	4b
		Ironpan soil	4
		Podzolic ironpan soil	4z
Soils with poorly aerated subsoil	5. Ground-water gley soils	Ground-water gley	5
	6. Peaty gley soils	Peaty gley	6
		Peaty podzolic gley	6z
	7. Surface-water gley soils	Surface-water gley	7
		Brown gley	7b
		Podzolic gley	7z

Table 17 Deep peats (peat 45 cm or more)

	Soil group	Soil type	Code
Flushed peats	8. *Juncus* bogs (basin bogs)	*Phragmites* fen	8a
		Juncus articulatus or *acutiflorus* bog	8b
		Juncus effusus bog	8c
		Carex bog	8d
	9. *Molinia* bogs (flushed blanket bogs)	*Molinia, Myrica, Salix* bog	9a
		Tussocky *Molinia* bog; *Molinia, Calluna* bog	9b
		Tussocky *Molinia, Eriophorum vaginatum* bog	9c
		Non-tussocky *Molinia, Eriophorum vaginatum, Trichophorum* bog	9d
		Trichophorum, Calluna, Eriophorum, Molinia bog (weakly flushed blanket bog)	9e
Unflushed peats	10. *Sphagnum* bogs (flat or raised bogs)	Lowland *Sphagnum* bog	10a
		Upland *Sphagnum* bog	10b
	11. *Calluna, Eriophorum, Trichophorum* bogs (unflushed blanket bogs)	*Calluna* blanket bog	11a
		Calluna, Eriophorum vaginatum blanket bog	11b
		Trichophorum, Calluna blanket bog	11c
		Eriophorum blanket bog	11d
	14. Eroded bogs	Eroded (shallow hagging) bog	14
		Deeply hagged bog	14h
		Pooled bog	14w

(Explanatory comments in parenthesis)

Table 18 Other soils

Soil group	Soil type	Code
2. Man-made soils	Mining spoil, stony or coarse textured	2s
	Mining spoil, shaly or fine textured	2m
12. Calcareous soils (soils on limestone rock)	Rendzina (shallow soil)	12a
	Calcareous brown earth	12b
	Argillic brown earth (clayey subsoil)	12t
13. Rankers and skeletal soils (rankers = shallow soils < 30 cm to bedrock) (skeletal = excessively stony)	Brown ranker	13b
	Gley ranker	13g
	Peaty ranker	13p
	Rock	13r
	Scree	13s
	Podzolic ranker	13z
15. Littoral soils (coastal sand and gravel)	Shingle	15s
	Dunes	15d
	Excessively drained sand	15e
	Sand with moderately deep water-table	15i
	Sand with shallow water-table	15g
	Sand with very shallow water-table	15w

Table 19 Phases occurring within types of Table 16

Suffix	Name*	Description
a	shallow	Predominately 30–45 cm depth of soil to bedrock.
c	cultivated	Considerable alteration to physical or chemical properties or to vegetation by former agricultural use.
e	ericaceous	Vegetation contains sufficient *Calluna* (dominant to frequent) to become a weed problem after planting.
f	flushed	Considerable enrichment with nutrients from flush water, as indicated by the presence and vigour of tall *Juncus* species, *Deschampsia cespitosa* or *Molinia*.
g	slightly gleyed	Subsoil slightly mottled or with grey patches.
h	humose	Topsoil contains between 8 and 30% organic matter by weight.
i	imperfectly aerated	Applied to gley soils with less prominent grey coloration than usual for the type (but which do not quality as 7b).
k	calcareous	With pH > 7.0 in the A, E or B horizons.
l	loamy	Used for surface-water gley soils and peaty gley soils where the texture throughout the profile is not finer than sandy clay loam.
p	peaty	Surface horizon containing more than 30% organic matter by weight.
	(or deeper peat phase)	Thickness definitions: 3p and 5p = 5–45 cm of peat 4p = 15–45 cm of peat 6p = 25–45 cm of peat (Note that types 6 and 6z have a peaty horizon 5–25 cm thick)
s	extremely stony	Stones occupy more than 35% of the soil volume.
v	alluvial	Soil developed in recent alluvium of sandy or coarse loamy texture.
x	indurated	Has strongly indurated material within 45 cm or surface. Implies loamy texture. Where indurated material is only moderately developed or is at depths of 45–60 cm, (x) is used.

* Naming soil types with phases: the preferred form is to give the name of the soil type followed by a comma, then the phase name in the usual order, ending with the word 'phase', for example: upland brown earth, shallow phase; peaty gley, deeper peat and loamy phase.

Rules for the use of phases (for brevity, suffixes are used here rather than names):
i.   Phase f, h, i and l are used only for gley soils.
ii. Phase g is used for brown earths, podzols, or ironpan soils.
iii. Phases which are mutually exclusive: e and f , c and e, h and p, a and x, v and x,
iv. Unlikely combinations: a and v, f and i
v.   When x or v is used, l is unnecessary.
vi. Where more than one suffix is used they are placed in the order: v, l, p, h, x, g, i, s, a, f, c, e.
vii. A soil type within Table 16 should always be given one or more phase suffixes where these are clearly capable of improving the definition of the unit, but there are numerous occasions where no phase is appropriate.
vii. The phase suffixes always follow the soil type suffix.

Appendix 5

Nitrogen availability categories in the poorer soils (after Taylor, 1991). (See Chapter 5)

Category A

Here there is sufficient nitrogen available for acceptable tree growth, despite the presence of heather. The inhibitory effect of heather on 'susceptible' tree species seems to be reduced when soils are rich in available nitrogen, and such species are unlikely to suffer any real check to growth, although there may be a slight yellowing of foliage in the two or three years prior to canopy closure. No fertilizer is required. Normally these are sites where the heather is mixed with fine grasses, such as *Agrostis* spp., *Festuca* spp. and *Anthoxanthum odoratum*, in the transition between grassland and heath; or weakly flushed sites dominated by bog myrtle *(Myrica gale)* and vigorous purple moor-grass *(Molinia caerulea)*; or sites heavily colonised by broom *(Cytisus scoparius)* or gorse *(Ulex europaeus)*. There is no need to kill the heather but it will usually be beneficial to control grass or other competitive weeds.

Category B

On these sites heather is the principal cause of nitrogen deficiency and successful heather control results in adequate availability of nitrogen for susceptible species. These are usually heathlands on more 'fertile' lithologies (e.g. basic igneous, phyllites, pelitic schists, New Red Sandstones and Greensands) or western *Molinia/Eriophorum* uplands where the heather is sub-dominant.

Category C

Heather is the dominant type of vegetation on these sites, but is not the sole cause of nitrogen deficiency. The low mineralisation rate is also a major factor and although heather control will result in a cost-effective growth response, it will not bring permanent relief from nitrogen deficiency and subsequent inputs of nitrogen fertilizer will be required to achieve canopy closure. This category can include peats where *Molinia* and deer-grass *(Trichophorum cespitosum)* are co-dominant with heather and certain heathland soils with low organic matter content.

Category D

The principal cause of nitrogen deficiency on these sites is the low mineralisation rate. Heather control does not give a cost-effective growth response. In fact, on many of these sites heather is either not present or very sparse. As an example, nitrogen fertiliser would have to be applied every three years to Sitka spruce from the onset of deficiency until full canopy closure is achieved (i.e. three to five applications). This category includes lowland and upland raised bogs together with some podzolic soils with low organic matter content on quartzose lithologies.

Appendix 6

Glossary of terms

Abundance

(Synonym = Cover) The vertical projection on to the ground of all the live, above-ground parts of the plant, as a proportion of the quadrat. The plant does not have to be standing on the quadrat to qualify.

Available water capacity

The maximum quantity of soil water available for use by the vegetation (assumed to be the tree crop), normally mainly within the rootable depth. The amount (usually expressed in mm depth of water) varies mainly with soil texture, stoniness and organic matter content. It is assumed that plants can extract water between *field capacity and wilting point*. Field capacity is the condition of the soil after it has been fully wetted and then allowed to drain under gravity alone for a couple of days. It can be thought of as a common condition of the soil, or a soil layer well above the water-table, in winter after a day or two of dry weather. At the wilting point the soil is sufficiently dry to cause 'permanent' wilting. The soil is so dry that it does not moisten the hands when squeezed. The available water capacity is increased if a water-table remains in reach of the root system, but it is difficult to estimate this contribution. Also, soils towards the base of slopes can be expected to gain moisture by downslope seepage given suitable substrate conditions (e.g. indurated subsoil, impervious bedrock suitably inclined). This can often 'increase' the soil moisture regime by one class, e.g. a freely draining soil that would be Fresh on the basis of its texture, etc., could be Moist where it receives seepage from above.

Constancy

See 'Frequency'.

Continentality

Continentality is the converse of Oceanicity (Birse, 1971). The Conrad index of continentality was derived for Britain from the mean annual temperature range and the geographical latitude and divided into four classes by Bendelow and Hartnup (1980). Thus their class O1 was the least continental and the most oceanic and had the smallest range of annual temperature and, other things being equal (e.g. latitude, elevation and topographic shelter), was the most windy, had the longest growing season, the highest atmospheric humidity and the smallest accumulated frost. Class O4 was the most continental and, again other things being equal, was least windy and had the shortest growing season, the lowest humidity and the largest accumulated frost.

Cover

See 'Abundance'.

Ecological amplitude

The range of climatic and soil conditions in which a plant can grow. Under artificial conditions all plants tolerate a wider range of conditions than they are found in nature, although not necessarily indefinitely. Competition with other plants restricts their range and tends to lead to species occupying characteristic 'ecological niches'. The concept of *tree species suitability* is, of course, an attempt to apply this in reverse by specifying the ecological niches of native and introduced tree species.

Ecological niche

See 'Ecological amplitude'.

Ellenberg indicator values

These are scores on a scale of 1 to 9 that give the

ecological preferences of each plant for various climatic and soil factors. A score of 0 for any factor is used when the species shows no clear preference for any part of the range. The relevant factors here are soil moisture, soil reaction (i.e. pH) and soil nitrogen for which Ellenberg (1988) assigned F, R and N values respectively. (See also Hill-Ellenberg indicator values.)

Eumull

Shows a rapid breakdown of litter, most disappearing within one year. The A horizon is well developed with strong structure. Earthworm casts are evident on the soil surface. The A horizon may be dark or light coloured.

Frequency

The proportion of quadrats on which a plant is recorded, irrespective of abundance. In the National Vegetation Classification frequency is scored I (0–20%) to V (81–100%). In ESC a scale of 1 to 10 is used, referring directly to the number of quadrats, within the set of 10, in which a plant occurs. Frequency is sometimes referred to as constancy. In the National Vegetation Classification those plants with a frequency of IV or V (7–10 in ESC) are referred to as the *constants* of the community.

Hill-Ellenberg indicator values

A series of ecological indicator values for British plants derived by Hill *et al.* (1999) from the original Ellenberg values. Hill-Ellenberg values for F, R and N exist for all British plants (i.e. the missing values have been filled).

Humus form

Organic layers or organo-mineral layers at the soil surface where leaf litter and other vegetable matter are being decomposed and incorporated into the upper mineral soil. Humus forms are classified according to the nature and thickness of the sub-layers and the agents of decomposition. Humus form is a sensitive indicator of the condition of the local ecosystem.

Lithology

The mineralogical composition, grain size and hardness of rock define its lithology. Geological age is not included.

Moder

Humus forms with three distinct layers, L, F and H, of which the H is diagnostic and at least as thick as the L and F combined. The transitions between the F and H and between the H and A horizon are gradual.

Moisture deficit

Is calculated for a station by subtracting potential evaporation from actual rainfall on a monthly basis, and summing the monthly deficits to find the maximum potential deficit for the year. Values are calculated for each year in a run of 20 or 30 years and the mean is taken. Moisture deficit is similar to the potential water deficit of Birse and Dry (1970) but the latter is calculated using long-term mean monthly values of rainfall and evaporation. Indeed, the values of moisture deficit for Scotland have been derived using a formula provided by Bendelow and Hartnup (1980) from values of potential water deficit produced and mapped by Birse and Dry (1970).

Mor

The least active humus form, in which fungal decay is more important than animal activity. There are L, F and H horizons, with a total thickness usually > 5cm. The H horizon is usually less than half the thickness of the L and F horizons combined.

Mull

A humus form characterised by a crumb to fine blocky structured Ah horizon of more than 2 cm thickness. Soil macrofauna, especially earthworms, cause rapid decomposition (one to two years) of plant residues.

Oceanicity

See 'Continentality'.

Oligomull

Slower breakdown of litter than in eumull allows a permanent, albeit thin, litter layer to exist. The A horizon is usually dark coloured because of the large content of organic matter.

Soil association

A term used by the National Soil Surveys for a collection of soil series occurring on similar lithology.

Soil reaction

Term sometimes used (e.g. by Ellenberg *et al.*, 1992) to denote soil acidity or alkalinity. Thus acid soils would be described as having an acid reaction.

Soil series

A term used by the National Soil Surveys to denote a soil type on a particular lithology. The term is approximately synonymous with a forest soil type without the phase differentiation.

Species abbreviations (see page 74)

Forestry Commission usage. Scientific names after Stace (1997) where possible. For the definitions of seed origins advice should be sought from the Tree Improvement Branch of Forest Research.

Species abbreviation	Common name	Scientific name or seed origin
SP	Scots pine	*Pinus sylvestris* L.
	Origins: West	
	Native	
CP	Corsican pine	*Pinus nigra* Arnold ssp. *laricio* Maire
LP	lodgepole pine	*Pinus contorta* Douglas ex Loudon
	Origins: ILP	Southern interior
	CLP	Central interior
	SLP	South coastal
	NLP	North coastal,
	KLP	Skeena (intermediate)
	ALP	Alaskan
SS	Sitka spruce	*Picea sitchensis* (Bong.) Carrière
	Origins: RSS	Oregon
	WSS	Washington
	QSS	Queen Charlotte Islands
	ASS	Alaskan
NS	Norway spruce	*Picea abies* (L.) Karsten
EL	European larch	*Larix decidua* Miller
JL	Japanese larch	*Larix kaempferi* (Lindley) Carrière
DF	Douglas fir	*Pseudotsuga menziesii* (Mirbel) Franco
GF	grand fir	*Abies grandis* (Douglas ex D. Don) Lindley
NF	noble fir	*Abies procera* Rehder
PSF	Pacific silver fir	*Abies amabilis* Douglas ex Forbes
WH	western hemlock	*Tsuga heterophylla* (Raf.) Sarg.
RC	western red cedar	*Thuja plicata* Donn ex D. Don
RSQ	coast redwood	*Sequoia sempervirens* (D. Don) Endl.
SOK	sessile oak	*Quercus petraea* (Mattuschka) Liebl.
POK	pedunculate oak	*Quercus robur* L.
BE	beech	*Fagus sylvatica* L.
AH	ash	*Fraxinus excelsior* L.
SY	sycamore	*Acer pseudoplatanus* L.
WEM	wych elm	*Ulmus glabra* Hudson
SC	sweet chestnut	*Castanea sativa* Mill.
SBI	silver birch	*Betula pendula* Roth
DBI	downy birch	*Betula pubescens* Ehrh.
ASP	aspen	*Populus tremula* L.
PO	poplar cultivars	D = *Populus deltoides* Marshall
		N = *P. nigra* L.
		T = *P. trichocarpa* Torrey & A. Gray ex Hook
CAR	common alder	*Alnus glutinosa* (L.) Gaertner
HBM	hornbeam	*Carpinus betulus* L.
SLI	small-leaved lime	*Tilia cordata* Mill.
WCH	gean, wild cherry	*Prunus avium* (L.) L.
RAU	rauli	*Nothofagus nervosa* (Phil.) Krasser